A Naturalist's
Life of New York

A Naturalist's Life of New York

WILLIAM BEEBE

DIRECTOR EMERITUS, DEPARTMENT OF TROPICAL
RESEARCH NEW YORK ZOOLOGICAL SOCIETY

with illustrations by
DONALD T. CARLISLE

THE BODLEY HEAD · LONDON

First Published in England 1954

Printed in Great Britain by
LOWE AND BRYDONE (PRINTERS) LTD., LONDON, N.W.10
for JOHN LANE THE BODLEY HEAD LTD.,
28 Little Russell Street, London, W.C.1

Foreword

THREE hundred and fifty years ago a walk along what is now Wall Street would have been a productive stroll for a naturalist. Today the seeker of wild life takes car or train and flees as far as gas or finances will permit. Nevertheless, the numbers of birds and fish and butterflies which still live their lives close to the city are surprisingly large. The veriest tyro can watch and list the migrant shore birds which in autumn supplant the human crowds along our beaches. Volumes have been published on the wild creatures of New York and others will follow.

But there is unseen life about our city: the creatures which pass in the night or swim in the depths, or which fly too high or too fast for our eyesight, or whose small size requires a microscope to become visible to us. Or consider those which are separated from our scant three score and ten by millions of years of time, their existence known only through the accident of discovery of bones or tusks or antlers in the geological graves of our city.

As unseen New Yorkers these deserve a place in the sun

of our consciousness. They help to keep us humble and at the same time they spur us on to make the most of our earthly span and our limited senses.

WILLIAM BEEBE

Simla, Trinidad
May 1953

Contents

CONTENTS

CONTENTS

To
Hugh and Marie Bullock

A Naturalist's
Life of New York

also by William Beebe

HALF MILE DOWN
ZACA VENTURE
BOOKS OF BAYS
HIGH JUNGLE

CHAPTER 1

Unseen Life of New York City

IT is sometimes worth while to stop and look about us in New York City and try to understand it as it really is. Ninety-two million, nine hundred thousand miles south (or north, east or west) of the sun, there floats loose in space a lonely pinprick of a planet, which is only one and one third millionth the volume of the sun. On a certain spot on this planet earth is, astronomically speaking, a fraction of a grain of sand which is known as New York City. The equator is 2450 miles to the south; the North Pole about 3000 miles to the north (although there are times when both these spots seem to have shifted to our very doorstep). If we travel to the point exactly opposite New York, we find ourselves among the waves of the South Pacific, southwest of Australia.

Except for a second at a time, New York, or any other city, is in no sense a stable, static, immobile thing. Considered as freed from present time and disregarding all future (for this is unceasingly becoming present), we might review it in slow motion from the beginning.

The only stable part of Manhattan is its foundation, for what kibitzers see when they hang over a fence, gazing fascinatedly at a vast excavation, are some of the most ancient rocks of old Mother Earth — igneous — cooled after the first spasm of planet conception. The basement of the most recent skyscraper rests upon stone which dates back two or three billion years. This figure is incomprehensible to our finite minds, so we can dismiss it with the information that it stretches back considerably more than a million times the length of our human calendar.

If New York's past could be compressed, the island would appear, to an onlooker, considerably like a frenzied fever chart. What was destined to become a supreme Urban Center has been tossed about, raised high in air, lowered until it was at the bottom of a mighty sea; it has more than once been hidden beneath a half mile of solid ice.

No Noah's Ark or zoo ever equalled the parade of life which has called New York's city "home." From anomalous creatures which were half plants, half animals, we skip through eons of lowly water and land creatures, ancient fish, reptiles, birds, mammoths and saber-toothed tigers to early cave men, and, in an infinitely shorter jump, to city folk of 1953. Today, we have our bogies, but imagine one of your and of my ancestors with a stone or a club, facing an angry saber-tooth! If our nth gran'ther got away with it, who are we to worry!

From cave men we pass on to Red Indians, Dutch, British, Colonials, and now the hodgepodge of races which we call Americans.

Shelters and buildings run the same gamut. First, caves, sometimes with wild beasts, sometimes with early humans as tenants. The first mortgage foreclosure was when a family of great cave bears ousted skin-clad near-humans from their air-conditioned cavern. There followed shelters, lean-tos, huts, wigwams and log cabins, succeeded by real houses and the first skyscrapers. These are in turn pulled down to give way to groups of gigantic modern cave-warrens concealed under the name of housing projects. Wild animal commensals are now confined to cockroaches and other unmentionables, mice and pigeons.

We speak of New Yorkers, but this assemblage is a flowing stream, forever going and coming, appearing and disappearing. Since the founding of the city, more than half a hundred generations have been conceived and born, have lived, and, as certain as the precession of the equinoxes, have died and been buried or their ashes scattered to make room for the next generation.

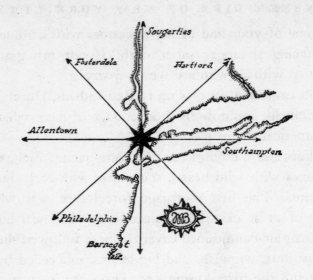

CHAPTER 2

A Journey into Our Own
No Man's Land

NEW YORK City, to several millions of us, is the focus of the universe — and not a bad focus, either. Like cave men of old we clamber up to our little cubicles, tunneled out of the street canyons, there to be happy or miserable, successes or failures, to live and to die.

Instead of the center of finance, or crime, or music, or of eight millions of crowded human beings, let us think of New York City as the center of a sphere with a radius of one hundred miles. Thanks to memory and imagination, we can conceive of this while immured in our four-walled cavern deep in the heart of the city. But there is a special reason for making this idea very real — as real as it actually is — so we might as well go where, quietly and at ease, we can see the sphere, or part of it.

I suggest one of two places — the top of the Empire State Building, eight hundred feet above the ground, or better still, the torch of the Statue of Liberty — my former watchtower for migrating birds. Here we are isolated far out in the bay and a hundred yards up — suspended amid earth, air and water, and here we can begin our game in earnest.

Start with the horizontal plane. We look eastward across Long Island, and begin our great circle not far from Montauk Point. Then swinging northward we box the terrestrial compass — Hartford, Reading, Philadelphia, and around to Atlantic City.

The circle would appear to offer more of interest to real-estate agents, population statisticians, petrol vendors, and politicians than to the naturalist. But when once we forget man's defacements and erasings of the old order of things, and seek out the few wild nooks and corners still remaining near New York, the pattern of the landscape changes utterly and we learn that, close at hand, there are scents other than gasoline and rubber, and sounds far different from those of riveting and radios. Details of the wild life existing near our city have been gleaned year after year by hosts of patient observers.

B

Watchers of the insects have recorded more than 15,000 species near New York within half the diameter of our circle, among which are 2000 kinds of moths and butterflies. Ascending the scale of life, we find that 260 varieties of fish make their homes in neighboring municipal waters above the twenty-five fathom mark. Beyond, and below this depth, and still well within our circle, we enter a no man's land whose inhabitants are still almost unknown to us. In two hauls, at the sphere's rim, due southeast from the Statue of Liberty, I once drew up, from great depths, fifty-five species of deep-sea dragonlike beings.

Before we go farther afield, let us give another thought to our home waters. I am writing this sentence in my studio in West Sixty-seventh Street, and if I lean far out of my window I can see the gleam of the Hudson River at the western end of the street. The continuity of the land on which my home is located may be compared with that of the water a few hundred yards away. Disregarding the insular character of Manhattan and continental bisection by the Panama Canal, the longest possible walking trail we could make would end at Bering Strait in the north and Patagonia in the south.

If, however, I went to the end of the street, climbed down into a rowboat and started out, the limits of possibility would encircle the whole globe. Unmindful of the possibility that I would be drowned soon after getting out of sight of land, there is actually open water between my little pier and the edge of the Antarctic barrier, the most distant waves of the Black Sea, the Amazon-drained eastern slopes of the Andes, the arctic foam churned up by swimming polar bears, and the flood of the Red Sea lapping the hot Arabian sands. The garbage-strewn tide swirling around the unlovely piles off my Sixty-seventh Street pier takes on a meaning and a dignity which it never had before. While on our continental jaunt we might conceivably climb to a height of four and a half miles up Aconcagua, yet after all, for our water world, the sky is the limit, what with clouds, waterspouts and rain.

Within the New York City sphere there live and thrive, together with ourselves, fifty-two species of amphibians and reptiles, of which only two are lizards, but fourteen are various kinds of snakes. Even within fifty miles of the city there have been recorded three hundred and seventy-odd birds, of which two hundred were found in Central Park. This exciting rectangle of trees and shrubbery is fast losing its attraction for bird life, simultaneously with the atmospheric pollution by automobiles and the steady closing in of lofty buildings. A half century ago sixty species of birds built their nests within its limits. Now only five or six kinds find it possible to rear their young between 59th and 110th streets.

Not a great many years ago I trapped eleven magnificent mink on the Bronx River in the Zoological Park, well within the city's boundaries, and had the experience of exchanging the raw pelts with a well-known Fifth Avenue furrier for a set of furs — exactly as two hundred years ago the Indians brought their catches, for trade with my ancestors in the early days of Massachusetts.

I know of one place within thirty miles of City Hall where wild beavers have increased to such an extent that they have to be trapped or killed off to curtail the damage occasioned by the flooding from their dams. Wildcats are apparently on the increase in two places within the circle, and only thirty miles away a bear recently reared two cubs. The last record is the authenticated presence of a wild black bear close to the northern end of the Kensico Reservoir, not much more than ten miles outside the limits of New York City.

Every now and then we are thrown into joyful excitement by the arrival of fellow human beings who have flown or climbed either very high or very far, or through stress of cold or night, and we cheer them and cover them with medals and city keys, and everyone is happy. If we long to see for ourselves what the arctic regions look like, we have only to fly less than three hundred miles to Mount Washington. Here we will find the summit well above tree level with stunted spruce like those of Fujiyama. Here summers are two and winters ten months long, temperatures may reach sixty below zero, and the winds howl past at one hundred miles an hour. In northern New Jersey, only a few miles from the heart of New York City is a small cave, which offers an easy descent to fifty feet or more. The air gets colder and colder, and at that depth it is possible to break off large chunks of ice and bring them to the surface, into the blazing sunshine and heat of mid-August.

We lift our eyes from the city horizon and let them play over the entire hemisphere of the sky — the home of day and night, of auroras, clouds, storms, sun, planets and stars. And now we begin to feel less the lords of creation. A gull soars easily past, bound for the utmost rim of our circle, and we begin humbly to take stock of our puny feats within celestial space. Upon our terrestrial circle we can ascend almost a mile, up Slide Mountain, without leaving the ground. From an airplane the earth is pure physical geography and mankind's utmost efforts reduced to smudges and unseemly blots. Only rockets and meteorological balloons can bring us word from naked space; thinnest of thin air and the bitter cold of the "Wind that blows between the Worlds," ninety degrees or more below freezing. The highest that any human being has been able to lift himself above the earth is a little under sixteen miles, although the altitude record for Primates is eighty miles up, held by a little monkey in a rocket. The inorganic rocket record is, at present, two hundred and forty miles. There is probably little to be experienced at greater heights but increasing cold and tenuousness of atmosphere. With old earth herself 8000 miles in diameter and the Pleiades blazing gloriously through three hundred light-years of space, these human efforts seem the superlatives of futility. (For all we know, the Pleiades may have gone dead and lost their light 299.9 light-years ago.)

If we falter at the thought of exploring the ultimate air

over New York, how infinitely more helpless are we in the face of the extremes of the nether hemisphere, stretching down and down from our crowded streets. Geologists and physicists can provide mental vision, and they assure us that thirty miles beneath our feet will bring us to a temperature of molten rock, twenty-two hundred degrees of heat, at which steel itself runs like water.

The utmost any man has achieved anywhere in the world is to sink a drill less than four miles beneath the surface, but when we realize that there is an increase of one degree of heat for every sixty feet of descent, the possibility of actual exploration underground becomes unthinkable.

In our beloved city, *facilis descensus Averno,* for many a street offers a gaping excavation for some new building. If the high-noon idlers who fringe each pit were geologically inclined they could learn many interesting things. Any sheer wall of newly opened ground is almost certain to show, near the top, the drift gravel and boulders brought from the Far North by the glaciers of past eras, or a treacherous layer of quicksand which has to be pierced before the solid rock foundation can be reached. This backbone of Manhattan, into the heart of which the stolid workmen guide their quivering drills, was formed in the very dawn of the world: 2,000,000,000 years is a conservative estimate of its age. Look at it as it crops out here and there in Central Park — quiet, gray, patient — and our individual worries will seem of less importance.

If we admit time into our circle, then the most familiar places are filled with interest. As we shall see in succeeding chapters, one of the oldest inhabitants of the city was found a few years ago, outstretched in his last long sleep near Fort Lee — a twenty-foot phytosaur, in appearance a slender crocodile, which splashed through mud and water in full vigor of life about 200,000,000 years ago. We examine his bones and try to reclothe them with flesh and movement; yet when we compare the few thousand years of the human calendar with the time separating us from this premunicipal reptile, it becomes, for us, one with the distance of the stars. More easily realized are other relatively recent inhabitants of Brooklyn, Long Branch, and Trenton — walruses, giant bison, enormous ground sloths, mastodons swinging along Upper Broadway and leaving their bones there — reindeer, horses, tapirs, musk oxen and peccaries. These all wandered within our circle less than 1,000,000 and many of them not more than 25,000 years ago.

Please take my whole theme of a hundred-mile sphere, with New York City at the center, as a real suggestion for thinking of common everyday things from a new angle. When you invert your head and look at a landscape, it appears brighter and fresher because, it is said, you are using rods and cones in your eyes which have been relatively unexcited since childhood. If, now and then, you think of San Francisco or Kalamazoo or your own back yard or window sill as a center of something besides humans and their affairs, you may do for yourself what the New York sphere could do: arouse new interest in what was beginning to become one of the worst forms of immorality — boredom.

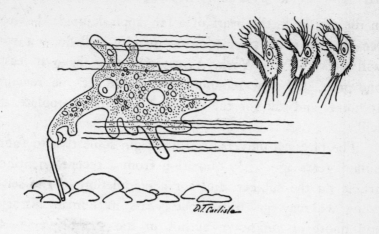

CHAPTER 3

City Magic

MAGIC is "working by power over the hidden forces of Nature," and even I, as a scientist, can sometimes work a very small magic with words. Nothing, of course, in comparison with fellow magicians in other fields — Edison, Bell, Daguerre, Marconi — all of whom would have been burned at the stake if they had worked their sorceries with waves, light, silver and electricity a few centuries earlier. Kipling was one of the greatest of all magicians, and so he could write that "the magic of Literature lies in the words, and not in any man."

I want to do some very small magics, and, as one who works by sleight of hand says, "You see, there is nothing up my sleeve," I will not ask you to go to a séance deep in the sea, or in the heart of a far tropical jungle, but to remain in a great city. Almost any city will do, but we will stick to New York. A magician must have at least one prop, so I now relinquish Space and let you remain at home, and ask for the use of Time, to manipulate at will.

"The physical universe had its origin some two to four billion years ago," is a quotation from a recent scientific article on the subject, and for a completion of the sentence we may go back 2000 years in human history and quote an unknown author in the second verse of Genesis: " . . . and the earth was without form, and void."

Having offered a formless preworld, we must admit that somewhere in space, even then, were the basic materials for the granite and concrete city we know today. Astronomy presents a vision of whirling, white-hot gas composed of isolated elements. Cooling and concentration brought these lonely inorganisms into closer relation, gas thickened, began to boil, then to flow, and hardened into rocks; hydrogen and oxygen flowed together and made steam and water; carbon, oxygen and nitrogen became air. This seems as good a plan as any!

We have now seen our potential Manhattan materialized, brought to a gentle simmer, and set aside to cool by the first great Cosmic Cook, Chemist and Creator. For this we must allot the whole of the first billion years. Then begins Act Two in the Drama of Creation. Just as the elements arranged themselves into air and water and earth, so somewhere, sometime, somehow a new sublimated synthesis came to pass, and what we call Life was born.

We are now started on our second billion years, but our thesis does not require any detailed account, eon by eon. Beginning with humble animal-plant blobs, we pass on to amoebas, sponges, corals, worms, starfish, clams, lobsters and spiders, bees and butterflies, fish, frogs, lizards, birds and mammals. We need go no further than the 250 acres of the Bronx Zoo to find today eleven out of the thirteen major groups of creatures living on the planet. This is really a remarkable thing, hundreds of species of wild animals, requiring no cages or special food or keepers. All eleven groups are on exhibition to any of us with sufficient curiosity.

Let us consider first, three primitive lives too small to be seen — all to be found in our lakes or our river; a lowly flagellate, a veritable mote of life, that whips itself about in the bottom slime, and may be so archaic, so dateless, that it simulates a plant in the daytime and an animal at night. Or the Amoeba, an immortal single cell, whose forebears appeared in the very womb of the world, and whose simple self typifies the stuff for the formation of all higher animals. Lastly, marvel please, with me, at the lovely Volvox which rolls with dignity across our microscope stage, a dignity well deserved, for in its being it mirrors the early, many-celled organisms which were to culminate in sequoias and elephants. Volvox is also exciting, even at this late, sophisticated date as adumbrating the beginning of sex.

When Is an Animal Not an Animal?

There are many grades and conditions of criminals. We may borrow and forget all about returning books and umbrellas and still preserve our freedom. I have seen a dog killed and also a horse, by men who are unhanged to this day.

But there are also crimes of omission, which loom large as our life goes on, and when the end comes, ignorance serves in no way as a palliation. We are taught in early childhood that the earth is round, but only constant reiteration renders the fact even temporarily credible. Never until we have circled our whirling bit of matter can we be quite sure. And when our last day dawns, what comfort to know that, wherever heaven or hell may be, any cosmic perception of our planet will awaken familiar memories.

We may have experienced the most ghastly horrors of bursting shell or crashing bomb, but all fades into firecracker comedy when once we have stood on the rim of an active volcano, and watched the lava blood-stream of Mother Earth. There remains in our mind no comparative emotion when we realize that this crawling, exploding stream is molten rock itself, and that the continuity of this planetary torch stretches back eons before men climbed down from trees, or crawled out of the sea, or even before a second cell was added to the original protozoan which was all of us — in the beginning. No human has fulfilled his manifest destiny of joy and awe in this life if his eyes have never looked through telescope or microscope.

We know that in the dawn of the world, after volcanoes had worked their will in the matter of islands and continents and the ocean had cooled to a reasonable temperature, the first signs of life became apparent. And at first the simple plants were not distinguishable from the first, equally simple, animals.

If you wish this incredible thing to become a matter of direct observation, go to some friend who owns a microscope, one who thereby has acquired more merit than yourself. Memorize this formula: "Show me, if you please, a flagellate combining holophytic and holozoic methods of nutrition." Or in the vernacular, "Let me see, under the lens of your microscope, a lowly, one-celled, living organism, which is a plant in the daytime and an animal at night." If he is a pleasant microscopist (as all the fraternity are) he will perform this miracle. He may only have to reach out for a few drops of water from a vase of flowers.

If we allow a toy balloon to escape, trailing a few feet of dangling string, we have a good imitation of the one-celled creatures known as flagellates, at which we are looking under the microscope. Only in these living motes of life the string or flagellum is lashing about and driving its owner in dizzy jerks through the water. If the diminutive balloon is greenish, it is on the plant side and with the help of warmth and sunlight can manufacture its substance out of a diet of raw chemicals, like any tree or leaf. But if the green matter is absent it is probably on the animal, or our own, side of the primeval fence. In this case it must find, capture and digest other plants or animals, exactly as we must do every day.

As we watch the infinitesimal specks, jerking here and there, we traverse a billion years, we see the miracle of the union of plants and animals, fairy stories assume more reasonable and possible explanations, and our stay on earth has gained something of importance.

The Last Amoeba

Man had a difficult time in the period just following the realization that he was himself. This set him apart from the glorious subconsciousness of the animals and burdened him with a troublesome responsibility as real today as it was then.

Tools had to be thought out and tried, or, more likely, materialized by way of the convenient theory of accidentality. Until then he had had to catch small beasts with his hands, or rob birds' nests or pick berries and fruit; if he did not do this he went hungry. He had to fashion skins to keep warm; he had to find a cave or a safe tree, or his enemies would straightway surprise and eliminate him. And there was the urge to seek, find, and cajole or carry off a mate.

Today all this is changed — almost all, that is, for it would seem we still have to use cajolery in the matter of a mate. But otherwise life is made up of communal bartering. I fashion the faltering words in this volume in the slight hope that I will receive in return from the publisher a bit of paper adorned with cabilistic signs. This, when transformed into metal, I may exchange for shoes, clothing, food and lodging, and even more paper to deface with more words.

Let us suppose the kindly owner of a microscope shows us what he calls an amoeba: a single, living cell, soft as gelatine, mobile as mercury. This, in fundamentals, is closely comparable with our cave-man ancestor.

An amoeba is an animal, and about the simplest one we can imagine. It exists on the borderland both of the animal kingdom and of human visibility. A very large amoeba is a fiftieth of an inch across, and so appears to us as a minute speck. Under the microscope it is just a blob of jelly, with an oblong object inside which we call a nucleus. I keenly envy the amoeba its method of locomotion. Slowly and tentatively it reaches out a slender fingerlike projection of itself, and if the fingertip finds life pleasant in that direction, by some mysterious beckoning, the news is conveyed and the amoeba flows and rolls fingerward, and soon it *is* the finger. And so on eternally in any one or all directions.

It feeds the way a snowball picks up dirt and pebbles if rolled across a bare patch of ground, and somehow the amorphous living jelly knows to reject, or to engulf and digest. Lacking eyes and other sense organs, yet the amoeba definitely turns away from an area of dilute acid or a very strong light. Water is as necessary for it as air is to us, but when its puddle-ocean dries up, the amoeba draws itself together, forms a watertight cyst, and waits months or years for water to come again.

Its incredible patience is explained by its method of reproduction, for all amoebas are immortal. After many days when it has dined to repletion and has become a large amoeba, as amoebas go, it hesitates in its leisurely life for a short time, and slowly and with quiet dignity begins to divide into halves. Within the hour, two complete amoebas are creeping about, each one perfect, each svelte, and no one can say, "This is the mother, that the daughter." We have seen the last generation come into existence, a final fractioning contemporaneous with ourselves on the earth. The first division must have taken place in the very well of the world; in our halting estimate, we murmur, a full billion of years ago. To our galaxy of the Milky Way, and to amoebas, it was yesterday.

This creature is 100 per cent American, having been an inhabitant of New York City ever since the ocean subsided. Neither glaciers nor droughts can exterminate it, and none of us, whatever our wishes may be, can avoid having from one to uncountable little amoebas in our home. Tap water is usually too fresh to be a comfortable abiding place for their simple life, but the water in a vase of flowers is, for them, sheer heaven. "As it was in the beginning, is now, and ever shall be, world without end. Amoeba," is not sacrilegious, but absolute truism to these firstlings of life.

I have compared an amoeba to the first man, because both were self-sufficient, independent, and somewhat totalitarian in that each individual is its own dictator. But it also reveals the muddle of ideas in that every amoeba is born free and equal, and hence has not gotten anywhere.

The moment we rise above amoebas in the scale of life we find glorious inequality. At first several one-celled animals remain bound together, but joined only by a lifeless stem, still isolated, still all alone in this great world. But soon real Siamese twins appear and sextuplets and so through sponges up to man, complex animals with a thousand separate functions performed by a thousand separate kinds of amoebas or cells. And this physical diversity and interplay mirrors our complex communal life of barter. Because I was lucky enough not to be born an amoeba — who knows — I may, after all, be able to buy some more paper!

Volvox, an Early Individual

To the layman, alga is seaweed and as such has no place in this chapter; it is all too visible as it drapes itself around one's neck, as we swim off the Long Island shore. To the better informed, algae merge (algae being several alga) on the one hand with our already familiar minute, one-celled

c

animal-plant, and on the other with the tallest plants in the world, the kelp which reaches up five and six hundred feet through the dark waters of the Pacific coast.

Every New Yorker will undoubtedly be interested to know that Wall Street is as full of algae as it is of fungus, thus affording satisfaction as a new fact, or an opportunity for humorous or sarcastic comment. While a pile on any wharf will furnish evidence of metropolitan seaweed, yet algae are almost omnipresent elsewhere, in ponds, streams and puddles, on marble and brick buildings, trees, soil, rocks, and even on snow and in the all but boiling water of hot springs.

To enjoy a televisionlike vista of an Algal World you have only to scoop up a few drops of green scum from the Central Park cattail swamp. If a policeman observes the operation you may have to explain away the suspicious-character ordinance before you can escape to your microscope.

When you collected the scum, the sun was shining, there was no breeze, a blackbird called lazily from the reeds, and butterflies fluttered past; someone dozed on a neighboring bench; peace and quiet filled the whole world. . . .

Let us now recall a flight in a plane well up over a modern battlefield with a large push in progress over the front lines. You look down and see tanks lumbering along, a few combat planes darting here and there, spraying as they go; hundreds of men running, stumbling, falling; the men hurling small objects which are not baseballs, which burst into beautiful star flames, yet are not fireworks; puffs of white and gray smoke billow and eddy, Morse codes of sparks shoot from the mouths of machine guns, flash and vanish. All this we see but in pantomime, not a sound comes to us above the roar of our engine.

Returning to a flattened drop of our scum under the lens of the microscope is not a violent break with the scene we have just left. Bright moons and stars of diatoms edge themselves along; slender, blue-green ribbons of algae wind about; orange yeast cells just rest and grow; more algae with bright green cells, round spheres rolling gently here and there, barbed-wire tangles of fungus litter the microscope field. And all about and through the scum move the animal attackers, slipper cells which are super-tanks, for they can turn and twist as they roll onward, forever slaying and sucking in unfortunate cells, both plant and animal; amoebas quietly but terribly engulfing what comes in their way, like living nemeses from which there is no escape. Rotifers with interlocking wheels of death never cease to draw down whirlpools and destroy small folk of the scum world. Many of the plants are as active as the animals and make their escape by sheer speed.

The next time we pass the cattail swamp we shudder as we realize the false peace and quiet which is far from being reflected in the battlefield of the calm green water beneath. We look down upon Wall Street from the spire of Trinity and see a very different scene; an ever-moving mass of human beings, passing and repassing, pushing but ever good-natured, looking at one another with friendly glances. If, however, we could focus a mental microscope, if we could make visible the thoughts, emotions, reactions going on within the brains of all these folk, perhaps there would materialize confusion, distrust, worry, doubt, which would almost equal the Pandorian escapes of the battle front or the park scum.

No battle ever waged without compensating deeds of unselfish rescue, of care and sympathy for enemy wounded; no human mind was ever beset with worry and doubt without some interlacing of altruistic thoughts. And from the rough and tumble of our scum cosmos let us rescue a minute speck of green and see if it cannot take our minds far from all ugliness and conflict.

A very lovely green sphere rolls slowly across our field of vision, and again we realize that in the heart of our city we may find hidden beauty combined with drama and unexpected surprise. One hundred and ninety-five years ago, Carl Linnaeus published his *System of Nature* on which modern classification is based. The old, time-worn volume before me begins with *Homo sapiens* and ends with *Volvox globosa*. As I look into the microscope and watch the turning sphere, I realize we two represent the alpha and omega of Linnaeus's conception of life on the earth. For our scum sphere is "none other" than Volvox, the roller, as it is well named.

Just as our flagellate trembled in the balance between

plant and animal, so Volvox represents the delicate and momentous beginnings of many-celled organisms, the first to end in such things as orchids and giant redwoods, and the second in hummingbirds and mankind.

Single-cell flagellates of a certain kind divide, but not altogether, and in time the increasing brood of brothers or daughters, or, more rightly, alter egos forms a flattened plate, which curves backward until an actual sphere, Volvox, has come into being. There may be five hundred or more of these attached cells, and if they all lashed out regardless, with their double whips, the sphere would twist and turn but never get anywhere. But in this Volvox something happens, one of the most significant things, next to the beginning of life itself, ever to occur on the planet. The five hundred cells are all connected with minute threads of protoplasm, and from the complete independence of each single cell there comes into being the faintest shadow of synchronization, of working and pulling to-

gether. The cells on one side (*any* side as far as we know) become slightly larger, develop sensitive eyespots, and for the first time there is a definite headness and tailness. Volvox may twist and turn, but it always progresses head first. Other cells elsewhere in this ring of living units go through the old-fashioned splitting into two, but in a few there is actually a hint of the beginning of sex as we know it today. In Volvox, from a drop of green scum stolen from Central Park, we have as good an example as possible of the origin of the many-celled individual.

CHAPTER 4

Too Old To Be Seen: The Records of the Rocks

The Manhattan Grubber

Long after all birth pains of Manhattan were past, our pleasant plot continued to have an exciting time. More than once it was completely submerged, with the Atlantic breakers roaring high above its water-soaked granite. Another time it slowly reared itself up until it was far inland, while the neighboring Hudson River cut a magnificent gorge for itself a hundred miles out at sea. Bitter cold alternated with such blazing tropical heat that palms and cycads flourished on the shores of Greenland far to the north.

Suppose we cross the Hudson River only as far as the great line of Palisades on the opposite shore and climb to the summit. Looking down from the rim of the mighty cliffs, we see the trains in the distance moving clumsily along like awkward worms while microscopic bugs of automobiles crawl even more slowly. Tugs and larger ships creep back and forth over the waters of the Hudson, and occasionally a plane drifts downriver, a tiny, gnatlike mote in the heavens. On the opposite bank is spread out a thin, frail crust of human habitations.

Before another hour of the future rushes upon us, becomes momentarily present, and eternally past, let us go in imagination back and back — ten, twenty, fifty, one hundred, two hundred million years. All human trace vanishes in an infinitesimal fraction of time; mammoths and stabbing tigers hardly less rapidly. Finally we sit up and look about us in what geologists call the Triassic Period. We are considerably lower on the Palisades than we were, for the lava on which we had been resting has not yet poured forth from its parent volcano. But the reddish sandy marl (which we can still see in the real today, halfway down the cliffs) is being formed on a sandy or muddy plain, dotted with scattered swamps and ponds, both here and across the river and beyond to the pre-zoo. Great ferns and horsetails are still in evidence but are giving way to the first dwarf conifers; the very beginnings of birds and mammals are in the making, the latest ancestors of ours being replete with reptilian bar sinisters still conspicu-

ous on their physical escutcheons. The life of this era within the hundred-mile circle around our city we know rather from footprints than actual fossil remains. We find the tracks of gigantic beings, slow and ponderous, to whose appearance we have little clue, and across them run tiny prints of timid defenseless creatures, fleeing for their lives. We find the hieroglyphics of worms, but no hint of the makers.

A few years ago there occurred a great piece of scientific luck near Fort Lee on these Palisades. There was uncovered a jumble of bones, so well preserved and distinct from one another that there was evoked from them a reptile, twelve feet in length, a creature covered with large bony scutes, with an incredibly long, cruel snout, armed with serried teeth. At first sight he looked like a crocodile, especially one of the slender-snouted gavials, those terrors of the Ganges. This dramatic find was the first Triassic New Yorker, our Oldest Inhabitant.

He was christened *Rutiodon manhattanensis,* which, eased into the vernacular, means the Manhattan Grubber. In life the Grubber was essentially a sprawler and swimmer, but in one decisive way he differed from living crocodiles; his nostrils were placed far back near his eyes instead of being at the tip of his snout. The teeth at the very tip were elongated and curved, so that the whole jaw has been compared to an elongated pair of tongs with nippers at the end. This assemblage of characteristics shows that in the probable absence of large fish and other toothsome inhabitants of the swamps and ponds, the Grubber had to grub for a living. With his nostrils so far back, he could feel about and burrow in the muddy banks, and seize the giant worms and other life, without any hindrance to his breathing.

And so, almost at the very spot where we are sitting on the Palisades, opposite New York City, a hundred thousand times as long ago as the duration of our calendar, the Grubber lived and splashed and ate and fought.

A Prehistoric Zoo

A zoo collector in prehistoric times would have gone mad with joy anywhere in New York, in the United States or elsewhere, and what exhibits could be shown! Imagine the Flying Cage filled with coal-age dragonflies whose filmy wings stretched almost a yard across, or with a flock of long-tailed, downy Archaeopteryx gliding from tree to wire, while diminutive dinosaurs, smaller than chickens, scampered gracefully about on their hind legs.

If a crate came to the zoo containing a Pteranodon we would be at a loss where to put it — that naked, dragonlike flying reptile with a wing spread of twenty-four feet. And while we are at it, let us revel in a welter of imagination at finding a leathery-shelled egg as big as a football in that same crate! How easy to visualize the sea-lion rocks removed and a Brontosaurus swashing slowly about with head and neck reared twenty feet above the heads of the visitors.

In those early days the reptile department of the zoo would dominate all others. There would be no birdhouse. Only a few small cages to accommodate loon- or ternlike feathered primitives with powerful teeth in their beaks. The aquarium would be large and varied, and a few giant amphibians would crawl about their enclosures. Our Botanical Garden neighbor would have a splendid showing of

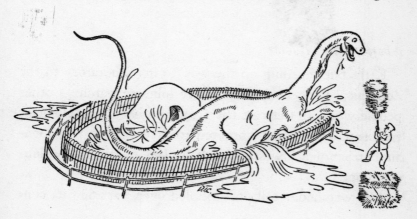

giant mosses and ferns, conifers and cycads, but not a single flowering plant.

Finally, the mammal department would be the least interesting of any in the zoo, exhibiting a few, small, furry animals, looking like arboreal shrews. In the wild, each was a veritable "Wee sleekit, cow'rin', tim'rous Beastie," creeping about at night on its search for insect food, in complete terror of its life from any reptile larger than an iguana. Far from being Lords of Creation, Makers of Zoos, we human beings, in this Mesozoic Era, were not even thought of. We would come along in due time thousands upon thousands of years hence, as the lineal descendants of these shrewlike, weakling, cockroach-eaters.

Having taken a long breath after this last thought, we plunge again into the past. The present is hurrying toward us; less than a million years are left before we ourselves walk upon the stage, but rocks and mountains, fossils and crystals all provide a decipherable palimpsest.

Manhattan Glacier

Early one morning on the way to my laboratory in the Zoological Park, I stood for many minutes watching other people work. In this case the great iron bars of an elephant enclosure were being uprooted to give way to the open-air barrier of a low stone wall backed by an inconspicuous slope.

As I watched, a tall post toppled over, carrying its concrete base and with it a great, rounded boulder. Thirty-nine years before, I had seen these strong bars placed in position, but neither I nor any man, living or dead, had seen the smooth, polished boulder when it was gently lowered into its resting place. For this, my third of a century would have to be multiplied six hundred fold.

In spite of a certain amount of activity during my five decades in the zoo, I have loved to loaf a good deal, and one of my favorite loafing places was on the top of the Rocking Stone. This is a secret vice, and very few people have ever caught me at it. At visitorless times, very early and late, and even occasionally at midnight when all the wolves begin to howl, I have perched topside of the mighty stone, and with knees drawn up, meditated happily on the Good Old Zoo around me.

I think of my exact position on the planet, eighty feet above the level of the seven seas, and at exactly 40°51′ North Latitude, and 73°52′40″ West Longitude, and finally comes the realization that my hard seat first settled into position at least twenty thousand years ago.

Even throughout so relatively short a stretch of time there were many strange changes — both of land and life. But within the extreme of a million years (what is geologically called the Pleistocene Period) several dramatic occurrences took place. Long before there was any human eye to see, incredibly great glaciers pushed away from the arctic regions, across Canada, down through New York and Connecticut and came to a halt almost exactly at what we now call the city of New York. The site of the future city was buried beneath hundreds of feet of solid ice.

Just as a snowplow in our city streets heaps up and pushes ahead of it a pile of dirty snow, so the glaciers ground out and pushed onward a mass of debris, from sand and tiny pebbles to gigantic boulders. Some of these rocks and stones were widely traveled foreigners: at Broadway and 190th Streets bits of fossil coral were dropped, which had been carried by the glacier all the way from the Catskill Mountains, vivid hints of incredibly earlier upheavals, from the old Devonian inland sea, whose waves rolled three hundred million of years gone by.

Four times, continents of ice pushed south, two of which drove across and overwhelmed the Manhattan area; and the last time, when the old stagnant ice finally melted, it lowered into place stones, gravel and soil, and with these the smooth boulder in the elephant yard, and even our Rocking Stone, dropping it gently, delicately. It came to rest delicately balanced, so that anyone can push against and sway its fifty tons, to and fro. Three times the ice sheets retreated, with long seasons of warmth following their trail. We are now living at the beginning of the Fourth 'tween Ice Age Summer.

When the force of the last glacier was spent, and the ice melted, the sand and gravel and boulders which were washed out and left, formed a narrow band of glorified glacial dump which runs through Roslyn, Jamaica and westward along the shore of Staten Island, Perth Amboy,

Morristown, and on and on till it ends near Seattle in the Pacific Ocean.

No matter how great our preoccupation with the vital problems of life today, we should not forget that we rub elbows with the past on every side. Those of us who were born and lived in the brownstone fronts, now so rapidly disappearing from New York and Brooklyn, might easily have had our first lesson in the past life of our neighborhood. Our front steps, cut from this red sandstone, became worn as the years passed, with the constant attrition of thousands of footsteps. But in this very sandstone, we still find footprints of gigantic reptiles left as they passed and repassed through the ripples of shallow water, or the marks of a driving prehistoric rainstorm, all imprinted a matter of a hundred million years ago. In the heart of the slab of our own doorstep may be the telltale tracks of dinosaurs, large and small, infinitely more exciting than those of the proverbial wolf.

We are here concerned mainly with the glaciers of later dates, for in their advance they drove before them the great hairy creatures of the following pages, too old' for us moderns to see. After the retreat of the ice, in the succeeding warm epochs, equally large and strange mammals came lumbering up from the tropics, and for a time lived and thrived among the forests which had sprouted upon the glacial debris.

A veritable cavalcade of wonderful animals lived in and around our present city and zoo, passing over the very rocks on which we stand or within galloping, hopping or flying distance. This we know: walruses frolicked off Long Branch; giant beavers and bisons, huge ground sloths, hairy tapirs, outsized peccaries and at least two species of saber-tooth, stabbing tigers all lived in our front yards, or within one hundred miles. Forest horses galloped as near as Throg's Neck, all-American steeds, unlike the immigrants of Cortez's time and today. Imperial mammoths, more than thirteen feet high, swung in herds past the Rocking Stone, but were seen by no living man there, although ancient cave men of France fought them, and refrigerating Siberian glaciers spewed them forth, perfect in flesh and hair. The last mastodon which walked through our zoo slipped into a peat bog three miles away, at Broadway and 141st Street, and died there.

Walrus

A tidal wave may break on a shore, rush far inland over sand and upland turf, and carry with it masses of seaweed. This jetsam is left high and dry and soon dies in the heat of the sun. On its return, the wave may uproot such desert-loving plants as cactus and carry them as helpless flotsam to a quick death far out to sea.

The slower, but no less implacable, onpushing glaciers of the past killed off all temperate and tropical animals in their path, or else drove them far southward, while the creatures which loved the icy blasts of the north found life pleasant and possible hundreds of miles beyond their usual haunts. Ground sloths and tapirs of former times came to New York from the tropics on a northward warm wave. In the walrus we have an Arctic creature which paralleled the glaciers as they marched southward. I say "paralleled" because a walrus is so aquatic that a drifting iceberg or the very edge of a low rocky shore forms his entire above-water cosmos. As the mastodons and musk oxen wandered slowly ahead of the rivers of ice, so the walrus in turn drifted and swam down the coast.

If time could be turned back, a herd of these strange creatures might have been seen by holiday-makers at Long Branch and Ocean Grove, New Jersey. In addition, however, to the difficulty of the years, we would have had bitter cold to contend with our enjoyment. At that time it would seem as if even the oldest inhabitant could not

D

have recalled more unseasonable weather, for walrus remains have been found as far south as Charleston, South Carolina.

Walruses do not thrive in captivity and only rarely do we see them alive in our zoo, but once there, these extraordinary beasts are never forgotten. No wonder the walrus was given a star part in Carroll's *Through the Looking Glass!* The remarkably long tusks which depend from the upper jaw remind us of what the saber-toothed tiger must have looked like. The walrus employs his weapons in a unique way — to loosen and dig up the great clam shells growing on the icy bottoms of Arctic bays. As with the tiger, the great tusks must get in the way of actual feeding, and it is said that the cheek bristles are so strong and hard that they act almost like teeth in extracting the flesh of the mollusks.

The lack of competition which the walrus enjoys in its particular niche of life has kept it remarkably unchanged, and the walrus of many thousands of years ago, which splashed in the water off Long Branch, is the identical species which lives today on the ice floes of Greenland.

Giant Bison and Beaver

"There were giants in the earth in those days" is a sound scientific fact, more true than some of the other geological statements to be found in Genesis. The million years before man stood upright, looked about, and began to say

"I am I," were more favorable to mammalian life than is the case today. When conditions began to change — occasional shortages of food, unseasonable shifts of weather and temperature — the more specialized and larger forms were the first to disappear. Two good examples of animals coming under this category of relative giants are prehistoric bisons and beavers.

A half dozen or more species of prehistoric bison once lived in the United States and some had horns of six feet spread, one of which grazed in the vicinity of our zoo. Another species of which we know very little, possessed horns, which from tip to tip stretched full ten feet. In eastern Pennsylvania, fossil bones have been discovered of giant extinct bisons, great creatures which made Buffalo Bill's namesakes look like runt calves.

I have sometimes imagined a gargantuan world in which there were beavers which could gnaw and fell trees such as the sequoias and redwoods of California, and with them

dam full-sized rivers. They would be to our living beavers as these in turn are to field mice.

Leaving baseless exaggerations and coming down to actual facts, there have been found in a cave at Strouds-burg, sixty-five miles from New York City, remains of a real giant beaver. From its skull and other bones we know that it was more than twice as large as those which have recently become re-established close to the city. With great, curving, yellow tusks this Pleistocene animal bulked as large as a black bear, about seven and a half feet in length, with a tail a yard long. If its weight corresponded, we would have a hundred and fifty or two hundred pounds of beaver, quite satisfying all our suppressed desires. There are reasons, however, to think that instead of requiring supertrees upon which to whet their crescent incisors, it may be that these early giants were terrestrial burrowers, or at most carved out homes for themselves in the banks of streams and rivers.

Ground Sloth

Only two groups of living mammals habitually hang upside down — bats and sloths. The latter range today over South America but do not get farther north than Nicaragua, a full two thousand miles to the south of us. But in intervals of the ice ages sloths of amazing size and appearance were not uncommon in the vicinity of New York City. There were many species and some were as large as elephants. They did not, however, hang upside down like their living cousins, for no tree would be strong enough to support them.

These ground sloths, belonging to the group called *Mylodon*, were about twelve feet in length — slow, massive, uncouth creatures, with probably as little brain and intelligence as the tree sloths of today. They lumbered awkwardly along through life, walking on their knuckles or the sides of their feet. They possessed claws of great size and strength, and with these the slothful giants could grub up roots and tubers and stretch up ten feet or more, when, braced on hind feet and tail, they could pull down leafy branches or uproot small trees.

The saber-toothed tigers were their chief enemies, but to overcome their victims it was necessary for the cats to penetrate a dense coat of long hair and a skeleton which was almost as solid as the armor of a medieval knight. If,

D. T. Carlisle

even in its death agony, the ground sloth rolled slowly over and managed to bring into play one of its mighty talons, nothing could save the tiger, and the encounter would be a fatal draw.

The ancestors of ground sloths came from South America where they were once abundant. No human being ever saw those which roamed about our city, but in a cave in the Argentine were found bones with attached skin and hair and evidences of food and fire — a ground sloth which must have been killed and eaten by men only a few centuries ago.

Far back in geological history some strange being must have lived, a push-me, pull-you of sorts with the habit of hauling down branches to feed on the leaves. One line of these descendants, instead of breaking the boughs, pulled themselves bodily upward into the trees, and the same thing is done by tree sloths to this day. A divergent line of offspring gradually became larger and heavier and learned to draw down or break off boughs and trees and so became ground sloths which have now passed forever from the earth. These latter, like kangaroos, found important use for massive tails as forming the third leg of a tripod for their stance. Even today, if we watch a living tree sloth climbing, we will see its short, stubby tail push and press against the bark and trunk, continuing an age-old habit which now is almost useless.

In a cave eighty miles from New York City remains of the great-clawed ground sloth have been found, the scientific name of which, *Megalonyx*, was first given to it by President Thomas Jefferson in a paper which he wrote in 1797. Knowledge of paleontology was in its infancy a century and a half ago, so little blame attaches to the cultured statesman for believing he had found the remains of a gigantic lion. Lion or sloth, the name is equally appropriate, and is in good scientific use today.

Hairy Tapir

Of all the creatures which formerly lived within the purlieus of New York and elsewhere on the Atlantic seaboard, the tapir was the strangest. Not in external appearance, for the tapir of a million years ago was much like the present animal of Central and South America, individuals of which are usually to be found in the paddocks of our zoo.

A tapir actually looks to be what he is, a sort of living fossil. A giraffe is a giraffe, and a zebra is indubitably a zebra, but a tapir reminds us of a number of animals not quite finished in all details. In number of toes — four and three — he has less than a bear and more than a camel; in aquatic ability he could drown out any deer, peccary or fox, but would scramble to the bank rather than compete with a hippopotamus. In length and mobility of snout, on the other hand, he far excels a pig, but is put wholly to shame by an elephant. So in any attempt at exact descriptive definition he tapers off to a prehistoric vagueness. Not long ago when I was in an isolated bay off western Costa Rica, a tapir suddenly walked out of the jungle onto the sand, and throughout the few minutes that he stood quietly watching, the whole scene seemed to shift back many millions of years, so primordially prehistoric did the creature appear.

Eighty miles from New York City, in the Port Kennedy Cave in Pennsylvania the remains of thirty-five individual tapirs have been found, Hay's Tapir, a species somewhat larger than living forms. These cave tapirs moved and had their being during one of the warm interglacial periods, and at least where our zoo was to be, they wandered about in herds or flocks or gangs, or whatever noun of multitude is applicable to a lot of tapirs.

The reason why we know so little of the ancestors of tapirs is doubtless because they are timid, forest- and swamp-loving creatures, and when they died their bones more often than not were destroyed by moisture and chemical action before they could become fossilized. We have some reason to suppose that extinct tapirs had a rather long coat of hair, the color of which perhaps was brownish, with a conspicuous, longitudinal pattern of whitish spots and broken lines. This is a sheer outrageous guess but it may be true. This color pattern, possibly ancestral, is that of the young American tapirs until they are about six months of age, when they shed it and assume the plain dark brown of the adults. As to the relative value of these two colors for protection, in the natural surroundings of the jungle and until the animals move, both the young and the old tapirs are intrinsic parts of their background. The snout or trunklet, although relatively so short, is able to function in many ways, such as rooting among muddy herbage, and, fingerlike, curving over and pulling down small branches.

Tapirs seem to have no powers of defense but possess very acute senses of smell and hearing. They are crepuscular, or actually nocturnal, and can move with remarkable quietness through the thickest underbrush. They are unlike their nearest living relations, the rhinoceroses, in being semiaquatic, and when danger threatens they take to the water at once and swim and dive with facility. Succulent tubers and leaves are devoured at the surface or even beneath the water. While all these facts refer to living tapirs, there is no doubt that millions of years ago the same statements applied.

In the game of odd- and even-toed which great mammalian groups have played throughout past ages, the tapir, true to form, while decidedly odd, agreeing with its fellows the horses and rhinos, yet is not wholly odd, not altogether even. There is no doubt, however, of its place as a non-cud chewer.

Like the lizardlike hoatzins of the American tropics, tapirs have found little competition throughout the ages in their diet and haunts, and hence have kept unchanged many characters of their far-distant ancestors.

Saber-Toothed Tiger

Long after dark, on a night when the snow glistens in the moonlight, we may hear, at the edge of some wood close to New York, the long-drawn out squall of a bay lynx, the largest wildcat left near our city. If we watch we may see the animal creep into the shadow of a fallen tree and perhaps leap upon a rabbit.

In days long past, in a warm interval between the eon-slow ebb and flow of glaciers, we might have seen in this very spot a mighty cat as large as a polar bear, mushing along on short but incredibly muscular legs. We know it today from its fossil bones as the saber-toothed stabbing tiger, but probably instead of being striped it was dun- or self-colored like our lynx. Strangely enough it was also lynxlike in possessing a very short tail, which by no possibility could be lashed from side to side as in living lions and tigers.

Its most remarkable characters were the two great canine teeth, eight and even nine inches in length, which hung down from the upper jaw, and gave it a most terrifying appearance. These were so conspicuous that they can be compared only with the long tusks of a walrus or the rapierlike fangs of a deep-sea viperfish. The lower jaw swung down and back to a full right angle, to give play to the brace of enamel blades.

In the saber-tooth we have the superfeline, more powerful than any living tiger, short-legged, overtoothed and overmuscled. The enormous tusks would be of little use against small game such as rabbits or squirrels. But we can imagine this dawn tiger stalking a slow-moving, massive mammoth or a giant ground sloth, springing upon its prey and killing it with deep slashes of the long dagger fangs.

The great body and leg muscles together with the unusually large talons would ensure an unbreakable grip on the back of the struggling prey, and the saber-tooth also has the advantage of five toes and five claws on the hind feet, one more than any modern cat can boast. So far we are reasonably sure of the method of attack. But the abnormal size of the cutting teeth had, through the ages, caused a radical reduction in all the rest, so that there were only ten teeth in all, as compared with the thirty-odd of its ancestors. With such a feeble armature, any efficient biting off of pieces of flesh or chewing them would seem impossible, especially as the huge fangs must have

D.T.Carlisle

constantly been in the way. So we must admit ignorance of the niceties of the feeding of the saber-tooth.

Probably the specialized diet brought about by the equally unusual dentition resulted in the extinction of these ancient tigers. This seems reasonable from the fact that when the great elephants and sloths vanished from the earth, the saber-tooths also disappeared. But in their heyday great numbers of saber-tooths ranged from California and Pennsylvania, south to the pampas of Argentina. We know that at least two species roamed the hills and valleys in Pleistocene times within one hundred miles of New York City.

Forest Horse

It is given to man to meditate, to reflect, to ponder and to speculate. At present if we in the zoo now and then go about our occasions with a dreamy, faraway look in our eyes, it is a sign of another of our prerogatives, we are absorbed in almost the greatest of mankind's mental accomplishments, the spirit of prophecy — the sublimation of Future Planning.

A young bird suddenly leaves warmth, abundance and parents and starts south to accomplish something about which it knows nothing. An orphan caterpillar only a few weeks out of the egg frantically enshrouds itself in a water and frost and enemyproof cocoon, because it is bound on the wheel of instinct. But our officers and architects can foregather in the zoo; they recall the past, they observe and criticize the present, and they create and plan new wonders and methods of exhibition.

Before the inception of these innovations, let us consider a few fading pictures of a pre-zoo, our own pre-zoo. For while retrospection is negative and static in comparison with anticipation, yet it is very necessary in the rounding out of any picture. Some of the scenes may be fairly recent, geologically speaking, others pertain to a time when the ancestors of these same officers were still anxiously concerned with not being devoured by the surrounding fauna: when speed — swift and unashamed — was more efficacious than inadequate brains, and climbing ability than still nonexistent spears: when an architect's ideals were wholly satisfied with a leakless and draftless cave.

Consider the forest horse.

Eighteen feet below the ground in an excavation at Fort Schuyler, the tooth of a horse was found a few years ago. In view of the hundreds of tons of refuse dumped hereabouts, this is not astonishing, although semifossil carburetors, spark plugs and tin cans might rather be expected. But this equine relic was found resting in and beneath glacial drift and sand and boulders, perhaps undisturbed since mid-Pleistocene — a matter of the patient passing of half a million years, which is considerably beyond the memory of the most ancient hansom-cab horse.

If the tissues of this steed of old could have reassembled themselves around the lone molar a few years ago, the horse might have seen the emblem of the World's Fair rising five miles away to the west, while to the northwest an equal distance would take it to its nearest living relations — in the paddocks of our zoo in the Bronx — the Asiatic wild ass and Prjevalsky's horse of the Mongolian deserts.

We can say with reasonable certainty that the horse around the tooth was about the size of a cow pony, with larger, heavier head and erect mane. Living in the east of our country it was very probably a forest instead of a plains horse, and hence dark in color of coat. Its hoofs, although dainty and smaller than those of the modern horse, showed no external difference from those of our own animals.

We know that several species of ancient horses lived in the vicinity of New York City, from their remains found in Camden, the Navesink Hills and the Port Kennedy caves in Pennsylvania, all within a hundred-mile circle. Although the fossil and recent species are so similar in general appearance, the Fort Schuyler horse is eons apart from our living animal. The tooth and its owner are a 100 per cent American, while all our race and plow animals are relatively new arrived immigrants. The years which separate the two are brief compared with the stretch of time behind the Schuyler horse to his early ancestor, which lived on the Wyoming plains not less than fifty million years ago.

A still earlier ancestor had full five toes on each foot, but the four and three of *Eohippus*, together with its fox terrier size, would provide sufficient new interest to our annual horse shows. What a marvelous sight would be a race between a half dozen of these Eocene horselets, smaller than whippets, each pattering around the tanbark on his fourteen toes! And what dramatic significance envelops the leg splints of a race horse when we see in them the actual remains of the second and fourth toes of millions of years ago.

While the cradle of the race of horses on the earth was in our own Middle West, yet the last individual died before Columbus discovered the Old New World. Cortez, a matter of a quarter of a century later, brought the first horse across the Atlantic to terrify the Aztecs, to mount the Apaches, and gradually to repopulate the whole of North America.

Today it looks as if a second extermination of our

horses was imminent, Dobbin and Pegasus both helpless before the inexorable advance of the automobile.

In any event, the single tooth dug up at Throg's Neck in Greater New York, was only four miles from our zoo.

Woolly Mammoth

Never has a word from some ancient, unknown tongue been transposed into a modern English noun which has acquired more appropriate significance than the name of these gigantic elephants. Only in their buried skeletons and in our imaginations can the mammoths of New York live again for us. But our French prehistoric ancestors knew them — fought them, killed and feasted upon them. Our appreciation of these pachyderms of the past comes straight to us from an artist forebear — Kipling tells us about him — "Ung," the lovable Pleistocene painter.

Except for the great development of hair and a smaller number of toes, mammoths are so closely related to living elephants that they have sometimes been included in the same genus. The imperial mammoth was the giant of all elephants, standing as high as thirteen feet and a half, and with tusks sometimes sixteen feet in length. Middletown, New Jersey, only twenty miles from New York City, was the home of at least one imperial mammoth, its remains being found in company with those of old-time sloths, peccaries and hairy tapirs.

Professor Osborn once wrote, "An insatiable *Wander-*

lust has always possessed the souls of elephants as it has those of the tribes and races of man." Whether or not this has to do with the unusual intelligence of both these inhabitants of earth we cannot say, but there is an interesting comparison of adaptability. In the cold of the northern regions the elephants assume layers of fat and a dense woolly coat. In the blazing heat of the tropics man develops a layer of protective dark pigment, and the elephant loses all his hair but a few scattered bristles.

In earthly wanderings the woolly mammoth, for thousands of years, excelled mankind, for from southern France he made his ponderous way over mountains and plains, through heat and cold, traversing Europe and the whole of Asia, crossing the temperamental Bering bridge to Alaska, thence on over Canada and the United States to our New England and New York. Here a last survivor was bogged down in North Plainfield, New Jersey, hardly

D.T.Parlide

E

twenty miles from Fifth Avenue, and about fifty thousand years before the first human suburbanite took his place.

In spite of all this shift of environment the woolly mammoth kept his specific individuality, and he is the selfsame kind that posed as models for the cave-dwelling craftsmen of old.

These ancient wights had no more written language than the mammoths themselves and for long we had nothing more to go upon than their crude drawings in the Dordogne caverns and our caches of bones and teeth. But fortunately for mammothologists, these hairy elephants, when on their interminable eastward hegira, wandered far north into Siberia. Now and then they would slide into a glacial crevasse and automatic cold storage. Here, through millenniums, they drifted slowly along in the heart of the glacier, entombed in the clear green ice, perfect in body, skin, hair, fat and other tissues. At the glacier's end they melted out, their flesh was devoured by wild animals and their ivory tusks treasured by strange men, cut into beads or scratched with the likeness of the owner.

In the course of time, scientists heard of the refrigerated mammoths, and in the Leningrad museum today, safely preserved from clothes moths, is a mounted skin, trunk, wool, bristles and all. In every way these mammoths were adapted to extreme cold, even to a large, rounded hairy cap on the top of the head, which concealed a seasonable storage of adipose tissue to be drawn upon in times of food scarcity. To these boreal mammoths, with their three inches of sheer fat, plus a dense suit of underwool and an overcoat of twenty-inch hair, zero weather must almost have been a necessity.

We read that when the tomb of Charles I was opened, one eye was perfect, and for a few seconds stared lifelike from the severed head before it collapsed. Even more dramatic is the emergence again into the air and light of day of a hairy mammoth, providing hundreds of pounds of fresh meat as nourishment for passing dogs and wolves, after lying in nature's cold storage for thousands upon thousands of years.

The Broadway Mastodon

Years ago I remember following a circus parade up Broadway. A half-dozen elephants swung slowly along in their preoccupied, aloof manner, forever immersed in some proboscidian reverie. They passed the many blocks solidly built up with houses, and on uptown plodded by the vacant spaces of high, rounded glacier-worn rock. One elephant seemed to me immense — it must have been full eight feet in height. All had been brought from India and with dignity and gentleness submitted their lives to be dictated by their human masters.

Thousands of years before, on this very spot, all that was recognizable of my circus parade was the sunlight, sky and air, and the same glacier-scoured rock. Yet about this time (years and months and days not having been invented) another elephant had wandered up this way, along some pre-Broadway game trail — a strange elephant, which we now call a mastodon.

On this particular day he stepped to one side, perhaps to pluck at a branch of hemlock. He suddenly felt himself sinking into a bog. The more he struggled, the more he sank. And there he died. A few years ago when the Harlem ship canal was being cut, a workman found one of his ivory tusks. It lay beneath four feet of sod and roots and twelve feet down at the bottom of the selfsame peat bog.

Very likely he was one of a herd of these great elephants, for in those olden days they were common hereabouts. The remains of more than one hundred have been found in New York State, some of them almost complete skeletons. Scallop fishermen have even brought the molar teeth of these beasts up from the bottom of the sea, sixty miles beyond Sandy Hook, showing that the great pachyderms wandered along the Hudson Gorge when it was still in the making.

The first unelephantlike thing we notice about our mastodon is his dense coat of dark reddish hair, showing him to be a camp follower of glaciers and a lover of ice and snow rather than of tropical jungles. Our only way to see a living creature even faintly mastodontian is to be on hand, in zoo or circus, at the birth of a baby elephant. The little chap is proportionately longer in body than its mother and is clothed in an astonishingly thick coat of hair, which, little by little, is shed and passes to the final resting place of the hairs of infant elephants. Finally there remains little more than a tuft of stiff, wire bristles on the end of his tail. The skull of a new young elephant also has more of a snout than that of his parents, and in this respect it distinctly reflects the elongated head of a mastodon.

A full-grown bull mastodon must have stood nine feet in height at the shoulder, and was quite fifteen feet long. The large teeth made possible the long life of these, as of living elephants, for an eater of grass exists only as long as its teeth. We know from fossil remains that these great mastodons suffered from tooth decay and from pyorrhea. The passing of tens of thousands of years does not diminish our sympathy for the pangs of toothache which must have emanated from a molar seven inches long, weighing perhaps twenty pounds!

One very interesting thing about mastodons was the presence of a small tusk at the tip of the lower jaw, some-

times one, sometimes a pair, reminiscent of a far-distant ancestor which was furnished with four long tushes of equal size, the tips of each pair crossing the other well in front of the head. Examination of the remains of food packed between the giant fossil molars reveals a preference for the needles of hemlock and spruce rather than for the softer fodder of deciduous leaves. In fact, five bushels of crushed twigs from these conifers have been found piled between the ribs of one fossil skeleton preserved in a peat bog. Mastodons were very wholly averse, however, to moss and marsh plants and even prehistoric blossoms.

Whether a mastodon trumpeted or squealed, what soft-bodied unfossilizable creatures he watched from day to day, what his newborn offspring looked like — these are forever lost to us, together with all the other mysteries of these cold old days, when wandering glaciers crept back and forth over the face of our land.

The Arctic Ox

Both in a quarter square mile in the jungle, and in a small circle in the ocean off Bermuda, I have found that concentration, in space, year after year, will yield an ample harvest of living creatures, many of which would never be observed in a short period of watching. If we could be endowed in time with a life of millenniums instead of years, the cavalcade of creatures seen on little Manhattan Island would be almost incredible. It would bear comparison with the double line of delectably smelling, painted animals, which we used to arrange, trooping into and out of our wooden Noah's Ark.

There are days of driving, icy blizzard, howling wind, deep snows, when a musk ox would be perfectly happy in our city, and indeed musk oxen thrive fairly well in our zoo. But a mammalogist ardently desirous of wild musk oxen would have to travel at least fifteen hundred miles, to the north of Hudson Bay or to Greenland. We can be certain, however, if only our observer had been on hand twenty-five thousand years ago, he could have gazed happily on musk oxen within the limits of Greater New York. We know that one died at Trenton, and others close by, so we can add its name to those past inhabitants of our pre-zoo, which fed within sight of where we now stand; being born, living their lives, fighting off great gray wolves as they are doing today.

The arctic ox is really a very good Noah's Ark animal, stiff and loath to move, covered with long, tangled hair, with short legs projecting straight below, and an unreal set of horns which grow across his forehead as if they were glued to a wooden skull. He is like a small edition of the bison, but adapted for life in a land of snow and ice. Until he is captured and brought south to be gazed at by creatures strange to him, he has never seen a tree, and has depended for daily bread on dwarf willows, grass and moss.

Unless rigidly protected, he will soon go the way of other large game animals and disappear. He cannot adapt himself to the unprecedented rifle bullet because of his instinctive courage, loyalty to his family and method of meeting his age-old enemies. These are bears and wolves, especially wolves. The musk ox bulls, instead of leaving the cows after the mating season, remain with their harems throughout the year. When danger threatens, the herd, large or small, falls into defensive formation, a rough circle, with the older, stronger animals in the outer row, all facing out, and the calves in the center. A single giant bull often walks up and down in front of this phalanx, ready to be the first to fight. Nothing but the pangs of actual starvation will ever tempt a wolf to attack directly, for only too well they know the skillful use of those sharp horns. When at bay before the dogs of the hunter, the resultant possible slaughter of the entire herd is unfortunately as easy as trap shooting.

Some time ago, on a cool, clear, snowless day, as I walked across the zoo, I stopped for a time in front of the paddock in which was a quartet of baby musk oxen, which Captain Bartlett had brought south. I tried to imagine their ancestors in front of the last giant glacier bearing down on this island of ours, the northern lights painting the sky, the vegetation scant and low, snow swirling before the bitter wind. As I watched, two of the little chaps trotted toward their brethren, fell into line, all facing toward me, in their pitiful instinct of self-preservation.

Fear soon passed from these arctic infants and one of them walked over to an empty food basket, looked inside, then daintily raised his hairy leg, and scraped patiently with his hoof at the bare wicker bottom. Here in our modern city, another habit has been unloosed, this time by hunger. The musk ox wanted food, and he did the only thing he knew, handed down to him by his fore-fathers. He was trying to scrape aside the snow and ice of the arctic from the food which should have been in the basket. He completed the imaginary picture.

These creatures saw the great solitary boulders which we see today; they saw the Palisades whose lava flows had cooled millions of years before. They lived in the shade of trees — trees, some species of which were soon to vanish, while others remained to shelter the first Red Indians and even to grace our parks today.

When the last ice age began to melt there came men of old, wading or canoeing across from Asia to Alaska, and then spreading over all the land, until we have the first record of them as Red Indians. Warriors and hunters from the Hackensacks, Tappans, Rockaways, Montauks, Navesinks, and especially Mohicans and Manhattans hunted and fought in or near the zoo, and probably spied out the land from atop the Rocking Stone.

Thus, as we have seen, throughout the last million years, glaciers, four of them, have shuttled back and forth across our continent. The last two reached New York itself, and the very last began its retreat only 25,000 years ago.

CHAPTER 5

Too Old To Be Seen:
The Records of the Books

Planets, Ducks and Indians

On the twenty-ninth of February 1940, I went out on the high roof of my New York home and watched the sun sink below the distant Jersey shore. More correctly, as the horizon of the earth slowly rose and eclipsed the last daylight of the month, a brilliant diamond speck blazed forth and, in the afterglow, Mercury shone clear. Following upward, along the ecliptic, the sublimated beauty of the great planetary chain was outstretched above me; Jupiter glowing mightily, Venus in unbelievable sparkling beauty, almost dazzling in her unusual size; Saturn, dimmer to our poor sight, but with the mystery of its whirling, cosmic star dust rings setting him apart in the heavens from all other bodies. Finally, Mars, whose red and fiery eye almost made real the horrible joy that a God of War must feel in looking down at present upon our poor humanity. If we include Uranus, which my small telescope reveals, and old Mother Earth herself, upon which I stood, here were eight planets glorifying the night sky. Twenty-one years ago a similar sight was visible, and again in the year 2002 our children's children will stand in the sunset light and look at the same planets — worlds without end.

I stood, quietly absorbed by this great cosmic spectacle, when two swift-moving motes across my eyes brought me back to focused consciousness. Flying almost at the level of my face, silhouetted against the dying afterglow, a brace of black ducks throbbed past. They were coming from their feeding grounds somewhere off Long Island, vibrating steadily and swiftly westward to some safe sleeping place up the Hudson. Here were two creatures living today, absolutely wild, a direct connecting link with the past. In my mind I went back one, two, three hundred years, then one and thirty more, to the evening of the third of September, 1609. All around where I now stood there were great primeval forests of oaks and chestnuts, and between the trees fires gleamed here and there, with Indians gathered about them. Instead of automobile horns, the howls of wolves came from the distance, and in place of the thousands of footsteps upon pavements, there were rustlings in the underbrush and drowsy murmurings of wild turkeys settling to roost.

Wild men and wild animals — all were living their lives as had their forebears for untold generations, undisturbed by any hint of what the morrow was to bring. But in my backward-cast vision I knew it to be the beginning of the end. For, as yet unperceived and unsuspected, there lay, at this moment, anchored in five fathoms off Coney Island, a little vessel with high poop, slightly built. In the failing light of this third of September, Henry Hudson leaned on the taffrail of *De Halve Maen,* looking down into the water and saw "many salmons, and mullets, and rayes, very great."

From my modern outlook high over the city of New York, I can see the former homes of at least six tribes of Indians whose place names locate them today after three centuries. On that momentous evening in 1609, the Indians living just out of New York in what we call Westchester, were Mohicans of the larger Delaware group, and their totem was a supernatural or enchanted wolf. On the west bank of the Hudson, the Mindsis and Hackensacks lived and fought under the sign of the real wolf. Even at this early date the place of the future city of New York was a mart of trade, and one of its Indian names was Laaphamachking or the place of bead-stringing or wampum-making. Wampum, or shell money, consisted of beads cut from sea-shells. The purple was more valuable than the white and was obtained from the inner part of the common clam, *Venus mercenaria*, the latter name meaning "given in exchange for value." The slow, laborious process of cutting, shaping and perforating the beads helped to give them intrinsic value. Large piles of clam shells with the purple areas cut out are still to be found on Long Island.

In Harlem, at Avenue A, between 120 and 121st streets there was once the workshop of a Red Indian arrow maker. Scores of arrowheads have been found there, some unfinished, others ready to be fitted to the shafts, together with heaps of imperfect, spoiled stones. Most of these arrowheads were made of a buff-colored flint, geologically unknown in this part of the country.

Up and down the game trails, widened for Indian use, and leading from village to village, went the pre-New Yorkers. They fished and hunted, and grew their maize, and when the corn meal was cooked they called it *suppaun*, the same name I heard used throughout my boyhood. They wore robes and coats and leggings of fur and skins, and fashioned bright feather headdresses. Moccasins were beautifully decorated, and copper necklaces were noted by the first white men. Warriors wrapped snakeskins around their heads with a dangling wolf's tail, and they painted their faces out of all recognition. They knew the secret of brilliant pigments — red, blue, green, brown, white, black and yellow. Their weapons were bows and arrows, war clubs and stone hatchets.

Hickory saplings were planted firmly in the earth, and the tops bent together and tied, archlike. Then split saplings were woven in and out of the walls, and the whole thatched with bark. Around the small villages were stockades of great logs, piled lengthwise and fastened into place.

Such in brief was the Indian's life on our island. Their only records were kept as colored patterns on strings of wampum, and their only religion was a devil worship of sorts. Innately friendly and generous, they were proud and quick to resent insult and injury, and when thoroughly aroused and angry they combined with bravery deep-seated treachery and cunning, and long nursed revenge. Small wonder that in immediate days to come, the ignorant, cruel Dutch seamen of those early days would soon turn the friendly advances of these unsophisticated savages into suspicion and hatred.

More than one hundred and twenty thousand sunsets have flared up and died down since Henry Hudson leaned on the rail of his little shallop, but if he raised his eyes from the mullets and "salmons" swimming beneath him to the sky above he must have seen at least some of the planets at which I was gazing, and sooner or later a pair of black ducks would have whistled past him in the lower bay, headed for the Hudson. As he watched them go, his hopes must have risen that the darkening, distant entrance was not the mouth of a mere river, but the passage to distant China — the Cathay of his dreams.

The First Manhattan Cocktail

The Reverend John Heckewelder, a Moravian mission-
ary at Bethlehem, Pennsylvania, took down, about the
year 1760, an account of the first interview of Henry Hudson with the Indians. This Indian tradition was published
in the Collections of the New York Historical Society.

Dr. Heckewelder wrote as follows:

The following account of the first arrival of Europeans at
New-York Island, is verbatim as it was related to me by aged.
and respected Delawares, Momeys and Mahicanni, near forty
years ago. It is copied from notes and manuscripts taken on
the spot. A long time ago [1609 would make it 151 years before]
when there was no such thing known to the Indians as people
with a white skin, some Indians who had been out a-fishing, and
where the sea widens, espied at a great distance something
remarkably large swimming or floating on the water, and
such as they had never seen before. They immediately returning to the shore apprised their countrymen of what they had
seen, and pressed them to go out with them and discover
what it might be. These together hurried out, and saw to their
great surprise the phenomenon, but could. not agree what it
might be; some concluding it either to be an uncommon large
fish or other animal, while others were of opinion it must be
some very large house. It was at length agreed among those
who were spectators, that as this phenomenon moved towards
the land, whether or not it was an animal, or anything that
had life in it, it would be well to inform all the Indians on
the inhabited islands of what they had seen, and put them on
their guard. Accordingly they sent runners and watermen off
to carry the news to their scattered chiefs, that these might

send off in every direction for the warriors to come in. These arriving in numbers, and themselves viewing the strange appearance, and that it was actually moving towards them (the entrance of the river or bay), concluded it to be a large canoe or house, in which the Mannitto (great or supreme being) himself was, and that he probably was coming to visit them. By this time the chiefs of the different tribes were assembled on York Island, and were deliberating on the manner in which they should receive their Mannitto on his arrival. Every step had been taken to be well provided with plenty of meat for a sacrifice; the women were required to prepare the best of victuals; idols or images were examined and put in order; and a grand dance was supposed not only to be an agreeable entertainment for the Mannitto, but might, with the addition of a sacrifice, contribute towards appeasing him, in case he was angry with them. The conjurers were also set to work, to determine what the meaning of this phenomenon was, and what the result would be. Both to these, and to the chiefs and wise men of the nation, men, women and children were looking up for advice and protection. Between hope and fear, and in confusion, a dance commenced. While in this situation, fresh runners arrive, declaring it a house of various colours, and crowded with living creatures. It now appears to be certain that it is the great Mannitto bringing them some kind of game, such as they had not before; but other runners soon after arriving, declare it a large house of various colours, full of people, yet of quite a different colour than they (the Indians) are of; that they were also dressed in a different manner from them, and that one in particular appeared altogether red, which must be the Mannitto himself. They are soon hailed from the vessel, though in a language they do not understand; yet they shout or yell in their way. Many are for running off to the woods, but are pressed by others to stay, in order not to give offence to their visitors, who could find them out, and might destroy them. The house (or large canoe as some will have it) stops, and a smaller canoe comes ashore with the red man and some others in it; some stay by this canoe to guard it. The chiefs and wise men or councillors, have composed a large circle, unto which the red-clothed man with two others approach. He salutes them with friendly countenance, and they return the salute after their manner. They are lost in admiration, both as to the colour of the skin of these whites as also their manner of dress, yet most as to the habit of him who wore the red clothes, which shone with something they could not account for, (lace perhaps). He must be the great Mannitto they think, but why should he have a white skin? A large hockhack or gourd is brought forward by one of the supposed Mannitto's servants, and from this a substance is poured out into a small cup (or glass) and handed to the Mannitto. The (expected) Mannitto drinks; has the glass filled again, and hands it to the chief next to him to drink. The chief receives the glass, but only smelleth at it, and passes it on to the next chief, who does the same. The glass thus passes through the circle without the contents being tasted by any one; and it is on the point of being returned' again to the red-clothed man, when one of their number, a spirited man and great warrior, jumps up, harangues the assembly on the impropriety of returning the glass with the contents in it; that the same was handed them by the Mannitto in order that they should drink it, as he himself had done before them; that this would please him; but to return what he had given to them might provoke him, and be the cause of them being destroyed by him. And that since that he believed it for the good of the nation that the contents offered them should be drank, and

F

as no one was willing to drink it he would, let the conse-
quence be what it would; and that it was better for one man
to die, than a whole nation to be destroyed. He then took the
glass and bidding the assembly a farewell, drank it off. Every
eye was fixed on their resolute companion to see what an
effect this would have upon him, and he soon beginning to
stagger about, and at last dropping to the ground, they be-
moan him. He falls into a sleep, and they view him as expir-
ing. He awakens again, jumps up, and declares that he never
felt himself before so happy as after he had drank the cup.
Wishes for more. His wish is granted; and the whole assembly
soon join him, and become intoxicated.

The Delawares call this place (New York Island) Manna-
hattanink to this day. They have frequently told me that it
derived its name from the general intoxication, and that the
word comprehended the same as they say the island or place
of general intoxication.

Time, as we know it, now passed swiftly. There were
fights between Indians, Dutch and Englishmen on or close

to the land our city occupies. One of my very special treasures is an almost perfect Indian arrowhead, which I picked up one spring, washed out of the side of the bank of the Bronx River near the falls in the zoo. It is made of flint of a pale yellow color, unlike any type of stone in the vicinity of Manhattan.

Red Indians and our Dutch predecessors knew and killed with arrows and blunderbusses many wild animals in and around the site of New York City. Here is the valedictory of four. At least two were served piping hot in the evening meals of the last century.

Gray Wolf

I once heard a wolf howl at midnight in the heart of New York City. In fact night after night, almost on the hour, as I wandered about the Zoological Park watching the nocturnal habits of the animals, the wolves would begin. The unholy yelpings of the coyotes instantly added their intermittent, irritating cachinnations, but through it all would arise the full-throated, drawn-out ululations of the gray wolves. The last wild wolf known to have lived in the vicinity of New York City was killed one hundred and thirty-six years ago.

Wolves, like Indians, are 100 per cent American. Twenty to thirty million years ago, on what are now the Great Plains of Kansas and Nebraska in our Middle West, ancient lines of wolfish forms began evolutionary experiments. Some became long-tailed and slender like civet cats, others superficially resembled bears and hyenas. Later, giant wolves appeared, as large as grizzly bears. But all these strains ran out in the course of time. Real bears and civet cats made good.

Finally about eight millions of years before today, there evolved an animal, which we call *Tomarctus*, which succeeded in life, and became the nth great-grandfather of all wild dogs and wolves. Our own wolf appeared sometime in the last half million years, while side lines were still dying out. One of these was that of the dire wolves of California, who had so little sense that at least five hundred of them, one after the other, fell into and expired in glutinous asphalt lakes.

The gray wolf does not seem to have been especially dangerous to the Indians of New York and elsewhere. As long as human beings did not keep cattle and horses, the

wolves were satisfied with their wild diet and let man alone. Only thirty-five years after the discovery of Manhattan by Henry Hudson, a Dutch resident of this city writes that the principal objection to keeping sheep in the colony was the number of wolves. From this time on, first Dutch and later English governments promulgated act after act for the destruction of these animals. One example will suffice.

After 1770 the following Order was issued:

Forasmuch as divers inhabitants of this colony have suffered many grievous losses in their stock, both of sheep and neat cattle, for the prevention of which and encouragement of those who shall destroy wolves in the said colony, and that the breed of wolves within the colony may be wholly rooted out and extinguished, be it enacted, etc., that in the County of Westchester there be paid twenty shillings for a grown wolf killed by a Christian, ten shillings for such a wolf killed by an Indian, and half that sum respectively for a whelp.

In these days, the Indians would have formed a Red Man's Union, and paraded up and down with birch-bark placards, mottoing: UNFAIR TO WOLF KILLERS! UNBOUNTY-FUL RESTRICTIONS! The wolves more than held their own, and in 1776 the bounty was increased from twenty shillings to three pounds sterling.

The reaction of gray wolves to the advent of white men is rather complex and a direct result of their level of intelligence. When lambs and calves first appear in their hunting range, wolves find these so much easier prey than fawns and other wild creatures that they become a serious menace. Wolves are soon thinned out by means of poison, traps and guns. Before long, however, there occurs a readjustment to these new dangers, and succeeding generations of cubs are taught to distrust anything tainted with the scent of human beings. At this point wolves begin to increase again, and only by the steady destruction of the forests and the spread of occupied land are they ultimately defeated. Among creatures of the wilderness, the crow alone excels the wolf in matching its wits against those of man. If wolves were smaller, or had the power of flight, they would put up an amazingly stiff resistance.

The family life of a wolf is as perfect as in any other mammal. Wolves mate for life, share in hunting for their young, and seem to be able to equip their allotment of four to eight offspring as thoroughly mentally as they do physically. In winter, especially in isolated uninhabited regions, wolves hunt in packs, and exhibit great shrewdness in the use of their numbers to head off or tire out their prey. In general resource they are well ahead of any domestic dog.

We breed monstrosities of canines; flatten their poor faces, shorten their legs to mere stumps, give them hyperthyroid eyes, strip them naked as the dawn or imbed them in such masses of hair that they can scarcely see; we can magic them down to muff size or up to giant boar hounds, make them permanent cowards or chronic fighters, waddlers or mile-a-minuters. Yet a dominating instinct at the back of their sophisticated brains, or what functions as such in their distorted skulls, will cause even a Mexican hairless or a Scotty to turn around and around before settling to sleep, as though to press down and smooth out the bed of leaves and sticks of some ancient wolfish ancestor.

Wood Bison of the Hudson

In the Paleozoic Age of jokes there was one which was almost as ubiquitous as that of the mother-in-law. This was about the Englishman, who, visiting the United States for the first time, gets his rifle ready and asks to be ferried across the Hudson River to hunt bison on the New Jersey side. This serves to emphasize the unexpected truth that there was a time when, if we stood on the New York shore, furnished with an adequate field glass, we could have seen herds of American bison silhouetted against the sunset on the tops of the Palisades.

Except for the south, the remains of bison almost box the compass around New York City: northeast, north, northwest, west and southwest; Cape Cod, Albany, Syracuse, Stroudsburg and Trenton. These were wood bison, like those living today in Canada, and their trails through the dense forests made man's journeys easier than they would otherwise have been. In 1773 the Pennsylvania bison numbered about twelve thousand, and the last one was killed in 1810 in Northumberland County. So if our Englishman's grandfather had traveled only one hundred and forty miles west of New York City he could have killed his bison.

Curiously enough, the first American bison to be seen by a Spaniard were in Montezuma's zoo in the Aztec capital of Mexico, and the first observed by an Englishman were living wild in what was to become the capital of the United States, in the District of Columbia. De Solis, who was with Cortez, writes:

> But nothing was more surprising than the sight of the Bull of Mexico, a rare composite of several and divers animals taking from the Camel the hump upon the shoulders; from the Lion, the flank dry and drawn up; the tail tufted, and the neck furnished with a long fringe in the manner of a mane; and from the Bull, the horns and the feet cloven. Outside of which, it imitates the ferocity of the last, in the vigour and the lightness with which it attacks.

Sir Samuel Argall, in 1612 at the head of navigation of the Potomac, found "great stores of Cattle as big as Kine, of which the Indians that were my guides, killed a couple, which we found to be very good and wholesome meate, and very easie to be killed, in regard they are heavy, slow, and not so wild as other Beasts of the wilderness."

These great, black wood bison, which once stood on the Hackensack shore and gazed eastward across the Hudson toward the future metropolis, stood six feet high at the shoulder, were twelve feet long, and weighed as much as a full ton. The head in all American bison is really of relatively normal size, as in ordinary cattle and oxen, but the great bushy hood, twelve inches long in the beard, gives the appearance of an unbalanced heaviness which is wholly belied by the quickness with which this great creature can spin around, ready for attack, almost in the space of its four hoofs. Blizzards and bogs were the bison's worst natural hazards. In fact, before the coming of the white man, wolves and Indians were their only enemies. The latter valued them too highly to slaughter them except for immediate food and for the warm robes which their hides provided. Also it took exceedingly good hunting for a horseless brave to creep close enough for his stone-tipped arrow to be effective, and yet himself escape the charge of a wounded animal.

Wolves were an actual influence for fitness in the bison as a whole, canine vitamins of sorts. On the outskirts of every herd or lesser assemblage, invariably could be seen one or more gray wolves, squatted patiently, tongues lolling, eyes unwinking. It was watchful waiting carried to the ultimate degree. The effect was twofold: first, the bulls and cows were never wholly off guard, and young calves were kept on the safe side of the old folks; and secondly, when a cow sickened, or a young bison injured itself, there was small chance of the weakening of the herd by any slowing down to the speed or even continued presence of the weakling. The keen wolfish eyes instantly spotted such a one, and sooner or later it was cut out and pulled down, while the strong, fit individuals continued to hold their own with deadly horn and hoof.

The European wisent, etymologically the antecedent of our word bison, is a larger, heavier-bodied animal, with considerably less mane on the fore parts. Caesar found them abundant in Belgium and Germany, but now only a pitiful remnant cling to the forests of the Caucasus, soon to go forever.

Historical times have known only the members of the family of wild cattle in America, but they are most noble members, and it is greatly to the credit of our conservationists that the bison — both plains and woods — are permanently preserved from extinction.

Reindeer

To children, especially in the memory of our own youth, it will be no news that caribou or reindeer once inhabited New York City. His was a poor childhood indeed, which cannot recall the "prancing and pawing of each little hoof." And while we may now correctly call the reindeer *Rangifer caribou*, there was a time when we knew that there were only eight of these wonderful animals, all with never-to-be-forgotten names. In the words of their driver:

> Now, *Dasher!* now, *Dancer!*
> now, *Prancer* and *Vixen!*
> On, *Comet!* on *Cupid!*
> on, *Donder* and *Blitzen!*

What the yak is to the Tibetans and the Bactrian camel

to the Mongolians, the reindeer is to the Lapps. And in recent years its usefulness as a domestic animal has been extended to the Indians and Eskimos of Alaska and Canada. This quality of complete adaptation to mankind is a very curious and unpredictable thing. A wild mallard duck becomes a puddle duck in two generations, while its very close relative, the black duck, remains forever wild; the Indian jungle fowl and the rock pigeon accept domestication with, I might say, open wings, while the Javan bird and closely related pigeons never relinquish their wildness. A moose or musk ox can with difficulty be kept alive in captivity while a reindeer submits to man's care — drawing sledges, providing milk and breeding freely, where horses and cows would freeze to death in a week.

With one of the densest coats of fur and hair known, hoofs which splay out into perfect bog trotters and snowshoes, and a digestion which prefers coarse moss, the reindeer is necessity and luxury to the people of the North.

Our American caribou is very closely related, in fact, most certainly descended from the European reindeer, and the latter name is equally appropriate. No wild reindeer are now to be found in the United States or probably Alaska, but on the great barren grounds of Canada untold thousands used to migrate south at the end of the short summer, to the pine forests where they could find the moss on which they fed. Early explorers describe the open landscape as darkened with them to the very horizon. In pioneer days of exploration, conservative estimates put the number at hundreds of thousands.

At the beginning of the last, or Fourth Glacial Period, migration on an infinitely greater scale took place. This time it was not to seek new pastures or to avoid plagues of mosquitoes, but an actual forced driving, slowly onward, by an immense, continent-wide glacier. Mastodons, musk oxen, reindeer, all were driven south, as inevitably as chips on a tidal wave. Myriads of the animals died, but many survived and found food and continued existence possible. In Connecticut, New York, Pennsylvania and New Jersey, we know the reindeer lived and died throughout hundreds of years. Later, the survivors followed the retreating ice northward, on and on, to the ultimate land, scarcely four hundred miles from the Pole itself. Today we find the remains of reindeer — skulls, bones, antlers — in the clay and peat bogs, sometimes within fifteen miles of Greater New York City.

Again, past ages have made scientific fact of part of a child's beloved legend. The reindeer have been New Yorkers, whether chronologically, during the receding of the final glacier of the Pleistocene, or when " 'Twas the night before Christmas."

Puma

In the more or less good old days, pumas or mountain lions were abundant throughout New England and New

York. One hundred and eighty-odd years ago, within one hundred miles of Philadelphia, a country drive and shoot under the pretense of decimating varmints, slaughtered "41 Panthers, 109 Wolves, 112 Foxes, 114 Mountain Cats, 17 Black Bears, 1 White Bear [albino?], 2 Elk, 98 Deer, 11 Buffaloes, 3 Fishers, 1 Otter, 12 Gluttons, 3 Beavers and upwards of 500 smaller animals." And it added that twice as many panthers escaped as were killed. The local Indians so resented this senseless killing of their staff of life that not long afterwards they ambushed the leading hunter and slew him.

One authority reported that in New Jersey there were many more pumas than wildcats, and a leading conservationist tells of reliable rumors that stray animals still lived in the Adirondacks between the years 1900 and 1909. But the puma has gone forever from New York City and holds its numbers only in such distant places as Florida, Louisiana and the West.

In old New York the Dutch settlers believed in the mountain lion in a realistic way, and when the Indians brought in the skins for sale they wondered at the absence of a mane, and why only lionesses were killed. Whereat the Indians, like their obliging descendants today everywhere in the wild, naïvely concocted the tale that the male lions lived in high mountains, many days' travel away, and were too active and fierce to be killed.

The degree to which any creature enters into the life of mankind is evinced by the number and character of its names. Ernest Thompson Seton has compiled the following list: Cougar, Puma, Panther, Painter, Catamount, Mountain Lion, Brown Tiger, Varmint, Sneak-Cat, Red Tiger, Silver Lion, Purple Feather, Deer-killer, Indian Devil, Mountain Devil, Mountain Demon, Mountain Screamer and King-cat. Of these names, more are devoted to the color and the voice than indicating that the puma was a dangerous animal. It fed, as a matter of fact, on every type of edible creature from grasshoppers to elk and buffalo, with a lamentable preference for the dainty flesh of young colts and calves when obtainable. But man and child seemed always immune from unprovoked attack.

I once stood in front of a cage in the Bronx Zoo close on midnight, and watched the tawny gray inmate as it gave utterance to a loud, long-drawn out, quavering cry which seemed as if it would never stop, and epitomized the essence of wild nature. To imagine it, multiply the most awesome yowl of a back-fence tommy by several times its amount of ominous, menacing, portentous, terrifying, appalling character, and you will realize what must now and then have frightened little Dutch babies fairly out of their cradles as they lay shivering in their father's log cabins in the wilds of Westchester many, many years ago.

Wild Turkey

To the modern city dweller, the American turkey is typified by the crowded, bedraggled inhabitants of crates, bouncing along our streets, on their way to some killing station for turkeys. This is especially true of the season of Thanksgiving (for everyone except the unfortunate birds). Then again we see them suspended in long dismal lines in butcher shops, indecently naked, fulfilling Plato's definition of mankind as "Featherless Bipeds"! Even the casual observer can tell that the birds in the crates are not wild turkeys, for if only a single, mussed tail feather remains, its broad tip will be seen to be white, and not, as in our splendid northern wild turkey, a rich rufous brown.

In the early 1600's turkeys were abundant everywhere in Manhattan and on Long Island, and their *gobble-obble-obble* must have often rung out on what was to become Fifth Avenue and the Battery. They held their own with the Indians, for their senses were keen, and their woodcraft far excelled that of the red man. Even the blunderbusses of the Dutch could hardly have reached the roosting places in the tops of high trees. So they continued to live and thrive, with frequent nocturnal forays to culti-vated fields.

Even before Henry Hudson sailed up the narows, the northern wild turkey was described by the French ex-plorer, Champlain. His testimony was as follows:

The savages, along all these coasts where we have been, say that other birds, which are very large, come along when their corn is ripe. They imitated for us their cry, which resembled that of the turkey. They showed us their feathers in several places with which they feather their arrows and which they put on their head for decoration, and also a kind of hair which they have under their throat like those we have in France, and they say that a red crest falls over the head.

The first official Thanksgiving, proclaimed by Governor Bradford of Massachusetts, was in 1621, and celebrated with the dedication to this feast of wild turkey. Twenty years later, a writer in New Netherland says of Manhattan:

There were so many Turkies and Deer that they came to feed by the house and hog pens, and were taken by the Indians in such numbers that a deer or three turkies were sold for a loaf of bread or a knife, or even for a tobacco pipe, but now one commonly has to give for a good deer six or seven guilders.

There must have been a certain day when a marauding gobbler on our island heard a liquid challenge from the very dooryard of a Dutch farmhouse. He answered angrily and proudly. The two birds drew together, and in the moonlight a battle to the death was waged — the white-tailed against the brown-tailed. The latter won, we may be sure, for the tame bird had weakened and degenerated during his long domestication. His forefathers had been brought by the Spaniards, more than a century before, from Mexico, and had spread over Europe. Now he had again crossed the ocean, and met the wild bird of New England.

Today, in the 1950's, the wild turkey, like the crow, still pits his wits against man's deadly snares and guns, and still continues to hold his own in wild and isolated forests. Long may his electric, vocal thunder be heard.

G

CHAPTER 6

Too Young To Be Seen

Sepulcher and Resurrection

I recently came back from a walk with a small bit of green rock, a snail shell and the egg of a sparrow. They lay on my desk, three inanimate objects, three pieces of limestone, of fascinatingly diverse shapes: the stone was worn smooth and flat, the shell was an exquisite spiral, and the egg was a superlative oval. I went away and not until night did I again look at them. The rock was unchanged, the snail shell had vanished, and the oval was no longer perfect — there was a nick in one side from which projected the minute beak of a young bird. So does dead lime provide sanctuary for life itself: in the first case a permanent home, in the second a sepulcher with certain resurrection.

Let us suppose that we have not the opportunity of netting an eel egg in the water over the Hudson Gorge and that it is midwinter when bird life is at lowest ebb, and even the sparrows have deserted the city. Yet we wish to see the living, moving, developing pageant of past life within a hollow shell, to perceive marvels greater than those promised by any seer within a crystal-gazing globe.

This is an easy thing for anyone to do at home. Fashion a small oven warmed by a lamp to a temperature of about one hundred and three degrees. Purchase a dozen fertile eggs from the nearest farmer and put them in your artificial setting hen. Every day or two steady an egg on its side in a box of sand, pick away the shell of the upper part, and bring to view the unseen bird life in your home.

While all the details will not be evident, a reading glass will make the magic more clear. In a shadowy way, in the sense of "as ifs," the whole pageant of life on the earth passes before us during the twenty-one days of development of the baby chick. At the very beginning we have the single cell, corresponding to the lowly amoeba, which lives its life today as it did in the fantastic past. Then we find two layers of cells and we think of the living sponges and jellyfish of the sea, which live and eat and work out their humble destinies with a mouth, a stomach and a very few cells. Worms are creatures that have a great many organs repeated a great many times, all much alike from head to tail, and in the developing chick we see tissues overrepeating themselves. For example, shadowy ribs to the number of fifteen pairs appear in the egg, all but five to vanish in the adult fowl. There is an elongate finfold along each side of the embryo which, at the proper time, clots up at two places, and the wings and legs appear.

When an egg-chick is thirty-six hours old it is only a quarter inch in length, yet the heart is already beating bravely, the eyes are conspicuous, and the brain is spread out all over the head, waiting to draw itself together into the adequate organ which will direct all the activities of chick and hen.

When the little bird is two or three days old we find structures that are derived directly from far-distant vertebrate ancestors. Gills are one of the most important, and for a brief space four pairs are distinctly outlined, before they melt and run together or dissolve into jaws, palate, earbone and tongue. The front limbs are at first rounded paddles of sorts, finlike; then fingers begin to be marked out, lizardlike, and finally the thumb and two fingers on which all birds support their wing feathers. Most significant, however, is a faint ridge which, at six days, appears inside the jaws. This is found developed in terns and ostriches and is probably the last hint of the enamel ridge which supported teeth in reptilelike early birds. So "hen's teeth" is not quite a fable.

Up to a week the small being might well be mistaken for the embryo of a reptile or a mammal, but on the ninth day hints of feathers appear, and the little white horn of lime on the beak. Nature has overlooked nothing, and like an axman who fills his lungs deeply before cutting through the last section of a great tree, on the last day the chick breaks through to the little oxygen chamber in the large end of the egg. A few gulps of the first air enter the unused lungs, and, not knowing in the least what it does, the incipient bird unites nerves and muscles and beak to a common end, the shell is filed thin and broken open and the egg-tooth has fulfilled its destiny.

One spring day a friend and I were walking through Central Park, and I remarked that in the tree overhead there were possibly eighty gills. My companion proffered nothing better than a patient silence. So, losing hope of any pleasant sounds of unbelief, I explained: English sparrow's nest, probably six eggs; robin's nest, very likely four; each embryo inside the shells passing through a stage with four pairs of gills inherited from a fishlike ancestor. Q.E.D!

Young Opossums

An infant opossum surely deserves a place in this chapter, for from the hidden recesses of its mother's body it is catapulted into an almost equally concealed pouch, in which for months it lives and absorbs vast quantities of milk. Instead of remaining unborn for the reasonable time of several months, it appears in the world after only twelve days, helpless, shapeless, more like a great pink grub than a potential backboned animal. My word "catapulted" is rather hyperbolic, for this amorphous little being possesses one perfect thing, an inborn instinct to creep or crawl in exactly the right direction, two or three inches to the waiting pocket. And not only this, but it has to climb upward all the way and at the end of the journey nose out a nipple from amidst a perfect jungle of hair. Its eyes remain tightly closed for the next six weeks, but its pouching instinct is as unerring as if rehearsed for a lifetime.

Birth control has no place in the economy of the opossum and a score of young may appear at one time, but this means tragedy, for there is usually room for only a dozen at the milk bar, and only first comers are served. Our pity is stirred deeply at the thought of the diminutive, blind little being, fourteenth in the bread line, fighting its way uphill and into an unknown cavern, only to find no unoccupied fount. For a time it creeps about, futilely pushing at its more fortunate brothers and sisters, and finally, succumbing to the pangs of hunger, tumbles out of the pouch and to the ground.

When newborn, seven thousand opossums are needed to weigh a pound, but the fortunate offspring in the pouch grow apace, and at the end of two months their weight may have increased five hundred fold. In the tropical opossums, before one litter has left the mother for a life of their own, another lot may be found occupying the pouch. So the patient, timid parent has need to search for recuperating food throughout the whole night, and anything edible — worms, millipedes, beetles, eggs, mice — is acceptable.

The opossum is a real F.F.V., if we interpret this as the

First Families of Vertebrates. Its early forebears are confined to Australia, while its more recent opossum connections call South America their home. The unusual early birth of the young places these animals in a most interesting median position in the mammalian scale of life. Below it is the duck-billed platypus of Australia which, reptilelike, actually lays eggs, while all higher mammals retain their young within their body until the offspring are wellformed.

Like some human first families, the opossum is rather decadent. It is also a confirmed pacifist, and, like Uriah Heep, most humble. It is an arrant coward and possesses that irritating habit of continuing indefinitely to turn the other cheek. Its only defense is a most realistic simulation of death, playing 'possum, together with a concomitant ability to recover from serious wounds. Among ninety-five skeletons of opossums, thirty-nine showed evidences of more or less recently broken bones, jaws, shoulder blades, ribs, legs and toes, all of which had successfully healed. The gait of an opossum is, at best, so wobbly and rolling that any induced limp would never be noticed, and as the animal is too much of a coward even to run from danger, accidental curtailment of speed is a negligible factor.

The spasm which, at the imminence of danger, turns the opossum into an apparent corpse, works havoc to those individuals living near boulevards and state roads, for no acting, however clever, will deceive or deflect an oncoming motor car. These lowly mammals seem to be the most frequent victims of such insensitive machines.

The opossum may also be said to suffer in silence, for its utmost effort in ordinary vocalization is a snakelike hiss. At the season of courtship, however, the male, at the highest pitch of passion, gives vent to his emotions in a series of metallic clicks, achieved by means of tongue or teeth. Just as in the dull intellect of some individual there may occur flashes of sheer genius, so in the opossum a remarkable habit has been recorded once or twice, the use of the coiled, prehensile tail to carry a handful, or rather tailful, of dry leaves to the nest in some hollow log.

Like some races of mankind, the common opossum, in spite of all difficulties, thrives under adverse conditions, and is increasing and extending its range northward from the center of distribution in the southern states. For half a century it has been common around New York City, and when introduced into Long Island and Connecticut has multiplied rapidly.

When we see a pack of hounds with heads raised on high, baying a hollow far up in a lofty tree, we may picture the opossum mother curled tightly up in her nest of leaves, and deep within her skin fold of a pouch, the dozen shapeless babies, patiently transmuting a constant stream of milk into another of the innumerable generations of opossums, generations which in the early history of mammals on the earth, stretched so far back into the remote past.

C H A P T E R   7

Too Small To Be Seen

Zoo Phyla

Even the most casual observer walking through the New York Zoological Park is aware that wild animal life is present other than the creatures living in the houses, behind cage bars or across open moats. Squirrels come to feed from the hand, gulls and sparrows fly overhead, now and then the head of a turtle is visible above the water of a pond, or a garter snake glides through the grass. In the spring, bullfrogs and peepers lift their voices from the swamps, and we can see small fish nibbling at floating crumbs in the Bronx River. In a word, in a day, we may see every class of backboned animals living on the earth, and sharing with us our own park.

Evolutionists divide all living creatures into a dozen to twenty great divisions which are called phyla, and are the larger branches on the tree of life. We will accept the lesser number. Incidentally these provide a shock for the human ego, for while various kinds of worms require four phyla, man, monkeys, whales, opossums, birds, snakes, frogs and fishes are all included in a single one.

Years ago when I was building up the bird collection in the zoo I spent some spare time messing about in the swamps and ponds and discovered that every one of the twelve great groups (with a single exception) lives and thrives within our boundary fence. The one absent phylum is called Echinodermata, the spiny-skinned starfishes and urchins. These are found only in salt water, and to complete the animal kingdom we must drive due east from the zoo for two miles, and there, near shore in Pelham Bay, we will find small starfish.

The other eleven groups which inhabit the zoo are "on exhibition" only when we search for them. A tumblerful of mud and decayed leaves from swamp or pond will provide us with several.

First come Protozoa, or one-cell animals.

Protozoans are such lowly creatures that some barely deserve the name, for some, as we have already seen, are really plants in the sunlight, and animals only at night. Other single-cells are housed in elegant and rococo shells, and while some live today inconspicuously in the waters of the zoo, others in past ages have piled up to make chalk cliffs, or dissolved into subterranean lakes of petroleum. The most interesting protozoans are those which cling uncertainly to one another, as if pretending to be creatures of a higher order. Some of man's worst enemies are one-cells, such as the minute bits of life causing sleeping sickness, pyorrhea and malaria. On the other hand, a host of these animalcules, all invisible, are fighting man's physical battles so stoutly that without their aid his very existence might be threatened.

So toward the phylum Protozoa we may feel the varying emotions of fear, curiosity, wonder, admiration, gratitude and amazement, even awe, but never indifference. That would only bring us down again to the mental level of Amoeba.

Phylum two consists of sponges, and it is surprising that in the brooks and ponds of our zoo sponges thrive, complete with fibrous skeleton, spicules and everything, except size, possessed by living bath sponges from the sea. In a fresh-water sponge it is the close clinging together of slightly differentiated cells to form a distinct individual animal, which raises it above the Protozoa.

Phylum three is as unexpected in our zoo as a sponge, for it includes jellyfish, sea anemones and coral polyps. As in some other groups a few species have found life possible and pleasant in fresh water, and there is a tiny, but beautiful and rare jellyfish which at any time may suddenly be found in our ponds. It has already appeared in a pond in Staten Island, and in the tanks of our aquarium. The delicate, little swimming jellies are only half an inch

across, but their name is *Craspedacusta*. We do not need
this jelly to make this phylum a zoo one, because a thim-
bleful of pond debris may contain many little hydras,
which are only coral polyps gone naked, individual and
acrobatic. These pleasing, active little beings with their
two definite layers of cells and permanent mouth, are fun
to watch as they loop along or briskly somersault across
our field of vision. It is a not unfelicitous thought that
hydras may possibly be somewhere near our main ancestral
line, on the way up from amoebas.

Phylum four includes the spiny-skinned starfishes and
sea urchins, which is the only group of this magnitude to
be absent from the zoo. Next in our animal review there
appears phylum five, the Bryozoa or moss animals. These
bear considerable resemblance to corals, the individuals
living in colonies which encrust leaves and sticks with a
moss or lichenlike covering. Under the microscope they
are graceful and elegant in form and motion. I have found
branched colonies of *Plumatella* in Cope Lake, reminiscent, on a miniature scale, of corals growing forty feet
down off Bermuda.

The next three phyla include worms of many and varied
kinds and appearances and it is a relief to be fairly certain
that the first three are probably side branches and in no
sense first families in our genealogy. (You will find their
special names at the end of this chapter.)

Phylum six embraces the flatworms, which may be
found creeping about on the underside of water-soaked

leaves, looking like minute tissue-thin slugs. Their heads are mere caricatures, for their mouths are far down toward the tail. They are harmless, and man and flatworms go their way together on earth in peace. However, these worms have near relations which are terrible afflictions of our race, including such organisms as liver flukes and tapeworms. The next group, number seven, is that of roundworms, most of which are minute, looking like white, coiled bits of thread. In the zoo they live harmlessly in the mud and water, and millions of them in the soil. Elsewhere, and especially in the tropics, they are dangerous parasites which cause the diseases of hookworm, trichinosis and filariasis. The members of phylum eight are much more pleasant creatures, which we may call wheelworms or rotifers. They are very abundant and active and go shooting across a drop of water by means of what looks like pairs of revolving wheels at the front of their bodies. This is an optical illusion caused by rapidly moving short hairs. This is also a consoling phylum in that it does us no harm. One of many interesting intimacies concerning rotifers is that in some species the males are extremely small and quite unable to take nourishment, while in other incredible groups this sex seems completely unnecessary and wholly nonexistent.

Phylum nine is the first of the larger divisions, the soft ones or Mollusca, which have bypassed the line of direct evolution to ourselves. In this group are the thousands of kinds of snails, slugs and octopuses which range from mountaintops to the depths of the sea. Within our acreage we possess both of the great classes, bivalves or mussels in the Bronx River, and univalves or snails on land. We may remark that there is always the possibility of pearls being found in the former.

To most of us the word *worm* means the common earth or angleworm, and together with leeches it belongs to phylum ten. Both of these groups are found in the zoo outside of cages. Earthworms are among the greatest friends of mankind, plowing and mixing the soil of our fields when we are too lazy or too ignorant to do it thoroughly. We ungraciously reciprocate by impaling the unfortunate angleworms on hooks as bait for fish. We can hardly think of these worms as beautiful, but cousins of theirs which live in the sea are as exquisite, colorful and graceful as flowers. They are also much more exciting, for they wave their petal arms about and can bud, blossom and vanish within a few seconds' time.

Earthworms are small and inconspicuous, living underground and seldom seen. Yet these lowly creatures represent a real and significant advance, especially in the development of successive segments of the body which persists throughout all higher creatures (even indirectly in ourselves, as in our series of ribs). Another important step is the presence of a ladderlike series of nerve ganglions. Whatever may be our present-day reaction toward the humble earthworm, we cannot escape the fact that some five hundred millions of years ago, the ultimate coming of mankind may have depended upon the success in life of some wormlike creature or its ancestor. This being, in turn, had at least the opportunity of looking back with mixed feelings upon his forebear, the amoeba, in still more distant times. So when next you encounter an angleworm creeping across your path, help him on his way, and for the amelioration of any overweening conceit, recite: "There, but for the grace of God, goes a member of the Zoological Society."

Of an unbroken ascent from Amoeba to ourselves there is not the slightest doubt, but the exact route is still so dim that the most recently accepted theory sidetracks the worms and invokes the minute free-swimming young of starfish ancestors which rowed themselves through pre-Cambrian seas some five hundred millions of years ago.

The eleventh phylum is Arthropoda, the joint-legged animals, and its multitude of members seems wholly out of all proportion when compared with that of preceding groups. The three-quarters of a million species exceed those of all plants and all other living animals. This group includes the lobsters, shrimps, crabs and barnacles, centipedes and millipedes, besides scorpions, mites and spiders, butterflies, beetles, flies, bees and all other insects. In size, abundance and diversity these completely overshadow the humble angleworms, but the pattern of fundamental step, up the tree of life, is relatively equal to that in the lesser group. This advance is most important, for we find here a complicated head with sense organs, and a brainlike enlargement of the anterior rungs of the ladder ganglions. The external skeleton and other characters, however, rule out all possibility of a direct line to ourselves.

Our zoo is rich in wild arthropods. Within a few minutes we could doubtless collect a pillbug, a millipede, a spider and a beetle and thus complete the tale of the more important classes. And as to insects, we know that every one of the twenty-three orders, from springtails to wasps, makes its home here.

Last in our march of life comes phylum twelve, Chordata or vertebrates, all animals with backbones. Here are five principal classes: fishes, frogs and salamanders, reptiles, birds and mammals, and we have already shown that all five are to be found living wild in the zoo. We human beings rather fancy ourselves as Lords of Creation, as the topmost twigs on the tree of life, and it is rather a shock to have our entire earthly population reduced to a single genus — *Homo*, which is the ninth diminishing division from the phylum of vertebrates.

In his *Animals Without Backbones*, Ralph Buchsbaum recognizes the following twenty-one phyla, an extreme of differentiation. In this list, man's phylum of the Chordata occupies a still more humble perch upon the tree of life; being one to twenty-one as to number of phyla, with a worm handicap of twelve to one. My consecutive dozen phyla are numbered.

> Protozoa — one-celled animals (1)
> Porifera — sponges (2)

Coelenterata — two-layered animals (3)
Ctenophora — comb jellies
Platyhelminthes — flatworms (6)
Nemertea — proboscis worms
Nematoda — roundworms (7)
Nematomorpha — threadworms
Acanthocephala — spiny-headed worms
Rotifera — wheelworms (8)
Gastrotricha — spiny worms
Bryozoa — moss animals (5)
Brachiopoda — lamp shells
Phoronidea — phoronis worms
Chaetognatha — arrow worms
Mollusca — snails, etc. (9)
Annelida — earthworms, etc. (10)
Onychophora — peripatus
Arthropoda — joint-legged animals (11)
Echinodermata — starfish, etc. (4)
Chordata — vertebrates (12)

Pollen

A man looks up at a giant sequoia, and sees the topmost branch sixty times his own height above him; the same is true of an ant if its eyes could encompass the summit of a ten-inch blade of grass. Another shift, this time of the imagination, but no less authentic, and we envisage the smallest existing plant, a bacterium, gazing at the pollen grain of a forget-me-not, and the sphere stretches up and up, again three score times as high as the lowly plant.

Let us slip below the level of the ant, but above the

H

bacterium, and come to rest in the world of pollen. When the Romans wished to speak of ordinary dust on their togas, they said, "*Pollen.*" When we allude to the male element of plants, we say, Pollen.

My pet monkey takes a morbid delight in plunging his face into a clump of flowers, although he knows he will invariably begin to sneeze. And so our cave men forebears probably suffered from hay fever, with no knowledge of its cause.

Today we are at the mercy of gravitation, yet we have no idea exactly what it is; about three millenniums ago the Assyrians regularly dusted the female flowers of the date palm with pollen dust, not knowing Why or What was taking place. From the earliest historical times, pollen was simply plant dust, for human vision is too weak and limited to resolve it. Not until about 1660, when Robert Hooke made a practical, compound microscope was the first pollen grain ever properly seen by man. Pumpkin pollen would have jumped to the eye for there are needed only one hundred and twenty-five to make an inch. But the pollen of forget-me-nots may still have been beyond Hooke's vision, for it is so small that an inch would require fifty-six hundred in a row.

Pollen grains are as durable as they are small, and have come to play an important part in our knowledge of past plant life on the earth. We can examine and identify under the microscope fossil pollen which blew about on the wind in the coal age, some three hundred millions of years ago.

And the pollen plunder from peat bogs enables us to re-construct the forests from a millennium past, down to the growths of last season.

This very old pollen was all wind blown, for there were no helpful insects in those days. Early creatures such as giant cockroaches and dragonflies with wings two feet across, would not have been much use to the flowers. If we come down the ages to one hundred million years, we begin to find serviceable insects, butterflies and bees evolved and ready.

As we look back it seems as if plants began consciously and intelligently angling for the help of these newcomers. Streamlined and winglike pollen structures were discarded and the tiny spheres covered themselves with sticky gum. Flowers set their caps for passing bees, appealing to every instinct and appetite — sensory, dietetic and comfort. They hung out banners and flags of the favorite colors of the insects; they shamelessly sprayed the air with alluring perfumes, and spread buffet luncheons with nutritious and sweet nectar. The susceptible bee alighted on the colored carpet of welcome, and found a wide, easy way to the banquet. While she feasted, she was powdered, tarred and feathered, with the precious pollen. Having thanklessly gobbled her free lunch, she sped away, by preference, to another blossom of similar color and fragrance, and there, unconsciously still, she dusted the female stamen with the pollen crumbs clinging to her hair and waistcoat. Thus she paid for hospitality and automatically ensured not only the continuance of the race of plants, but guaranteed a supply of food for next year's generation of her own tribe of bees.

As in all general progress in evolution, hundreds of plants joined in this new venture, and reciprocity between the two kingdoms developed into a smoothly going concern. But, as is also sadly true, many flowers waved their flags in vain, the perfume of these floral old maids was wasted on the air, their pollen shriveled. No suitors called. With the never-say-die spirit of wild life on the earth, these failures tried to return to the good old days of wind fertilization of their ancestors. Today we find the grasses of our prairies as well as such plants as pig and ragweed and sagebush, again successfully casting their pollen upon the breeze. Only the shreds and tatters of the past glory of petal-flags remain to tell of the flowers' failure to go modern.

We have telescopes and microscopes, but what a miraculous boon would be automatically adjusting lenses, which would enable us to look out and across a meadow, and see pollen enormously enlarged and with microscopic clarity!

Even a balloon must have some kind of a take-off, and as we watch the clouds of pine and oak pollen pouring like smoke across the fields, we realize that, like gliders, they have the advantage of a high start. Such minute objects as pollen grains can almost escape the pull of earthly gravity. Many more lowly plants would fare but ill if they just dumped their pollen upon the sea of air. So we find exquisite adjustments intended, not to beguile heavier-than-air insect agents, but to take advantage of the best meteorological conditions. The least hint of breeze or wind will insure the widest distribution, and a resultant decrease in the terrific odds against the grains falling on fertile places.

If to the magnification of pollen at a distance, could be added increased sensitivity of hearing, we might, in our own woods and fields, detect or even be deafened by a continuous barrage of exploding pollen-cannon. Some shoot straight up like bombs or skyrockets to burst in mid-air; others are discharged short, trench-mortarlike batteries, and still others are snapped off like the old-fashioned slings and stone hurlers of the Grecian soldiers.

Careful observation reveals delicate mechanisms, hair triggers whose operation is wholly dependent on exactly favorable weather conditions. The artillery remains spiked and silent if the day is still and wet, but when a dry wind springs up, whole batteries loose their salvos in the eternal battle of life and death, and the continuation of the race in the world of plants.

Striking similes have been drawn between the appearance of pollen grains, and nuts, seeds and the minute oceanic animals on the one hand, and inorganic crystals on the other. The majority are more or less circular, but the sculpturing and ornamentation are without end. Makers of designs need never leave the realm of pollen for lack of inspiration.

As I look at a collection of pollen, I am reminded of baseballs, sea urchins, cucumbers, magnetic mines, starfish larvae, embryo tadpoles, checkerboards, the surface of the moon, coffee beans, grains of wheat, grubs, birds' nests, dumbbells, bananas, butterfly eggs, and prehistoric Mayan toys; for while most of them are rounded, the surface is either smooth, or covered with nodules, pits, reticulations, ridges, spines, cones, triangles or many-sided, beautiful designs.

Every pollen grain, so far below our range of vision, is perfect in itself, living but asleep, ready to waken if, by a ten thousandth of a ten thousandth chance, it should fall on the stamen of a female flower of its own species. Some must achieve this, otherwise the world of plants, and very shortly afterwards mankind, must perish utterly from the face of the planet.

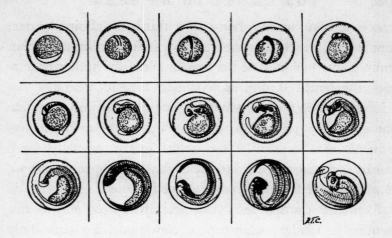

CHAPTER 8

Too Clear To Be Seen

ANY attempt to consider the unseen is severely handicapped if it is confined to life, to living things. The inorganic world is dominated by transparency. A full half of the old Pythagoras classification of elements, fire, water, earth and air, are fundamentally invisible. The ultramarine of the surface of mid-ocean, or the turquoise-green over coral reefs excites the color recipients in our eyes, but a tumblerful of water from either area is invisible. If we put a drinking glass under a vacuum pump it will appear to be (as in truth it is) filled with little or nothing. Let air pour back into it, and to our eyes, the tumbler is still empty. It is a wonder that we ourselves are not translucent, for our lungs are filled with hyaline air and of the whole content of our body two thirds or about 65 per cent is composed of water. Indeed, if it were not for the complete pellucidness of the lens and vitreous humor of our eyes, the world around us would be forever unseen.

The solid earth upon which we live seems wholly opaque, but even this residue can develop transparency for many minerals are "crystal" clear, while gritty, gravelly sand can be metamorphosed into clear glass, and opaque carbon can be resolved into diamond as well as coal.

Elemental transparency disappears when the entities intermingle. Under undisturbed conditions we can look down through water as much as sixty feet beneath the surface and see the fish and corals. Or we can look upward through the three hundred and fifty-odd miles of atmosphere and on and on to the spiral nebula in Andromeda, one million five hundred thousand light-years away.

When water and air are mingled, when gravity and wind and evaporation and planetary motion mix and churn them up together, then they will become translucent or even opaque. Thus are born fog, which can blot out the world; snow, with its innumerable, lovely crystals; clouds which give us sunsets; rain, generator of the rainbow; and bubbles, those fragments of air which are enmeshed by breakers into foam.

It is well known that in nature there are many protective adaptations. Leaves, flowers, bark, lichens, twigs, rocks and sand — all are imitated by beings who hope to be mistaken for something other than they are, or to facilitate the stalking of prey. The extremes of this bid for continued life are the creatures which imitate *nothing*. In tropical jungles there are skeleton butterflies which have lost their wing scales and with them color and pattern, and when they alight, they vanish from sight, for whatever leaf or flower is beneath shows clearly through their diaphanous wings.

Within the limits of our New York circle are still more striking examples, but to find them we must go as far out to sea as possible. The calm surface of the ocean is the ideal place for transparency. A simile of what goes on there is a partly frozen pail of water, when only the sense of touch reveals the skim of ice on the surface. We may look over the gunwhale of a boat and see only clear water, but the sweep of a net may reveal sea life as transparent as air or water or glass.

The champion water-content creature is a jellyfish. Lift one out into visibility and place it on a thwart in the sun, and in an exceedingly brief period of time, there remains only a thin skim of glairy slime. The personality of a jellyfish, its individuality, is composed of a mere one or two per cent of its bulk, all else is perfectly good old salt water. Imagine a hundred and fifty pound man whose visible ego weighed only six pounds! Our brain is more than half water. Comment is unnecessary!

If we draw nets day and night at sea, we find a world of creatures whose physical makeup is fashioned to convince prospective enemies that they are nonexistent. Some of the largest crayfish start out in life as larvae, flat as a sheet of paper and with elongate legs and long-stalked eyes which act like a swimmer who spread-eagles to provide more floating surface and buoyancy. Thin and absolutely flat as these beings are, they must contain some sort of nourishment, for great seven foot tunafish feed upon thousands of these bits of life. Squids do not play fair for they can so manipulate their pigment cells that they deck themselves from minute to minute with a great variety of spots and bands or solid blue and red colors. In addition, at will or at night, they can become so transparent that a swallowed fish in the stomach appears to be still at liberty in the sea.

In our glass menagerie we occasionally come across schools of worms, like diminutive arrows, with fins like feather guides, which are wholly transparent. What an idea for medieval warfare (if only glass had been invented), to fashion transparent arrows, which, in trajectory, might have been as invisible as the infinitely swifter future bullet.

Well off shore, at depths where only drowned men have reached the bottom, live strange sea eels. Many are nameless and as yet unseen by human eyes, but we know that they exist for at certain seasons of the year the eggs of these eels rise slowly to the surface and drift about in the full light of the summer's sun. They are only an eighth of an inch across and too transparent to cast a shadow.

These mysterious eggs are found within our New York

circle as well as in the waters of the Gulf Stream and in the ultramarine slicks off Bermuda and the high seas. They float for a time on the surface and if not swallowed by some creature to whom all flesh is meat, they sink again as they begin their development. They finally hatch into larval eels of sheer glass, transparent and, in the water, invisible bits of life. Their story deserves a place in our tale of the unseen.

I scooped up an egg one day in a fine-meshed silk net and gently transferred it to a small glass dish beneath the lens of a microscope. With no care other than the replacement of evaporated salt water, the egg lived, and from a sphere of inert yolk developed into a young eel. This at length broke through its egg tissue and swam forth, a half inch, transparent sliver of life, muscled and eyed, and armed with great fangs.

Soon after our egg had been deposited in the black depths of the sea, together with thousands of brother and sister eggs, its single cell divided into two. The double cell of our eel egg becomes 4, then 8, 16, 32, 64, 128, and so on until the paler end of the egg appears as a finely divided froth of thousands of cells. As the increase continues, the cells spread out and downward like a skin or film over the entire surface of the yolk.

During the succeeding seven days and seven nights within the confines of this small cosmos of glass dish and microscope, there is visible the panorama of cell to living creature, which throughout all the ages of life upon the earth has repeated itself from the first separate cell up to you and to me. All that is necessary to observe this for ourself is to return again and again to the microscope.

When the skin of cells completely envelopes the ball of yolk, there appears an elongate nick in one side, which grows slowly, becoming an open trench and continuing until it has reached the north and the south poles. Swiftly the action changes; a series of little crosshatchings shows the very start of the backbone; two minute bulges at the north pole presage the eyes.

One of the most exciting things is to watch for the first beat of the heart, uncertain, more of an uneasy spasm. Soon comes another and a third, and the next time we look, it is probably going full speed, about one hundred and fifty beats to the minute. At this rate, if the eel should live for a period of ten years, this two-chambered bit of twisted muscle will have more than 788 million beats to its credit.

Thirty-two hours after the beginning of activity in the egg, a strange thing happens. The entire yolk commences to revolve slowly on its polar axis, carrying with it the embryo eel, until, as we look down through the microscope lens, we see the young creature lying exactly along the horizon contour, and in this position the growth in all parts of its body is distinct and clear to our eyes.

From now on, the chief superficial change is the steady absorption of the yolk, altering in contour from a full moon to a gibbous and finally to a slender crescent. The head becomes greatly enlarged, with the brain pushing upward and forward, and the eyes never ceasing to increase in size. The body elongates more and more, and the incipient vertebrae increase until they pass the hundred mark, when if all else fails, we know it for a young eel. The tail gradually lifts clear of the yolk, and about the third day the head is free. The heart is beating steadily, and so clear are all the tissues that the yolk substance, primitive blood of sorts, can be seen as it is pumped through the heart and on to the various organs. The tiny jaws are ferocious-looking at this stage, armed with long, needlelike fangs.

One day, or more truly within a certain minute of time, the head and tail meet around the circumference of the egg, but growth does not stop and in the course of the next few days the young eel extends once and a half times around its glassy prison. The yolk becomes reduced to a slender thread and the muscles of the infant are in full function. It twists and thrashes about, coiling and wriggling, hour after hour, long before it is actually ready to hatch.

I have spoken of the jaws as armed with long, slender fangs, but for a time these are nothing but shadow fangs, embedded in a beak which in curvature and relative size is like that of a macaw. Like the ribs of an umbrella the supporting fangs curve around. The reason for all this is apparent later on.

When the yolk is well absorbed, the little fish shows almost all the external characters of its race. The parrot jaws open and close, champing together like the gums of a toothless old man. The eyes move in their sockets, as yet seeing nothing for there is nothing to see, my egg floating alone, all by itself, in its secondary ocean of laboratory glass. The round pectoral fins fan the fluid in the egg, useless as yet, but ready for their future balancing function. Even the hairlike sensory organs along the sides are developed, all aquiver for the recording of pressure waves in the water of the open sea, warning of danger, hinting of food.

The last act approaches. The embryo alternates violent contortions with periods of quiet. The movements appear haphazard, but if we observe carefully, the head with its great beak comes to rest again and again near the same spot. Now and then the eel coils up tightly, so that its body forms two and a half small, flat spirals. It then uncoils with a slow, scraping motion, the head at right angles to the egg wall.

If our patience holds out, we will notice that the place fretted by the beak after a while is marked by a slight bulge on the outside of the egg. Now, during periods of quiescence, the neck muscles move and strain, and the sharp beak continues to rub up and down against the inner lining. The egg is not nearly as clear as it was at first, the reason being that the outside is covered with a growth of bacteria and other organisms. Now and then our eye catches the scurrying movement of a herd of minute life life on the rim of our visual ability. Any puncture in the surface of the egg, however minute, during the last week, and all this microscopic horde would have poured inside and ended the life of the eel. I have watched such a death, and a horrible thing it is, although the pain and suffering were wholly in my imagination, and not in the half-formed nerves of the eel.

At last the parrot beak fulfills its destiny and cuts or pushes through a slit, and with frantic convulsions the eel leaves the egg to the inrushing bacteria, and lies quiescent, not in the open Atlantic, but in the half ounce of salt water beneath my lens. For the next few days it learns to swim and do all the things which newly hatched eels have done for the last millions of years. The membrane shrinks away from the fangs and leaves them bare, relatively longer than those of a saber-toothed tiger.

As I watch this vital being, a full half inch long, eyes functioning, gills breathing, moving about, trying to dive to deeper regions, my mind goes back a single week to the amorphous yolk and the madly dividing cells. It seems as though a vision had been granted into the very heart of the origin of life.

CHAPTER 9

Too Disguised To Be Seen

IF it interests us, while on a walk through parks or wood-
lands near New York, we may divide wild life into two
categories. There are those which we can see — a yellow
butterfly, a bright blue jay, a squirrel — and those which
we are certain are near us, and which can only be per-
ceived by accident or through a thorough search. We rest
our hand on a tree trunk and a bit of bark detaches itself
and flutters away on the lichen-hued wings of a moth.
From beneath our very feet a feathered bomb of a wood-
cock, to the last instant invisible in its dead leaf plumage,
springs up and rockets off.

An excellent way of humbling any conceit we may
feel, is to examine a bush, leaf by leaf, and list what we see
of living creatures. Then, holding an open, inverted um-

brella beneath, shake the same bush thoroughly and see the world of life of Small, which we pass on every walk.

The simplest class of Hiders may be called the Under Leafers. They need no color or posture protection, and fear attack only from above. They never seem to sleep for, at the slightest disturbance, they slither to the lower side of another leaf, or flee momentarily topside.

In the midst of a search for Hiders, there may suddenly loom into view a slow-walking bug — a true bug — blazing with blacks, reds and yellows. We might almost establish a new category — Too Blazing To Be Overlooked. This is warning coloration (having nothing to do with our present thesis), which probably indicates that the owner is unfit to be eaten by the most famished, omnivorous feeder. Equally conspicuous is a small crab spider when seen on a green leaf, but it is actually seldom to be found in such a place. By accident we may discover one crouched flatly in the heart of a flower, legs spread, in wait for the first unwary bee or fly. In this position the spider vanishes from casual sight, merging perfectly with its background. A further refinement is an ability to change color from white to yellow within a few days' time. Thus a white spider need never lie in ambush among the petals of a yellow flower, or vice versa.

Perhaps the ace of Hidden Ones near New York is the well-named walking-stick insect. Its scientific tags show an appreciation of its dominant appearance — phantom, apparition, spectral. It looks like a twig, it feels and poses

I

like one, it moves like one. Its antennae, head and body are twigs of varying shapes and caliber, its six legs are side twiglets. Its position is never regular. Two legs may be resting on nothing, dangling in mid-air, or the two forelegs may stretch out straight in front, aligned with antennae and body.

When we have discovered a walking stick and gently lift it from its perch we find further adaptations to all sorts of concealing and confusing poses. The sides of the legs have furrows and concavities of varying shapes, and when we manipulate it like a loose-jointed doll we suddenly find that all six legs may be pressed close to head and body, the curves fitting perfectly around eyes and joints and bumps, producing a twigletless single stick twig.

It may be greenish or brown, but always a twig. In the wind it sways, exactly as a twig sways. However, when slightly disturbed, it sometimes gets its meteorological time signals confused, and it proceeds to sway when the air is perfectly still, thereby exposing itself to detection and danger, if we happened to like the taste of insect twigs, or wanted the walking stick for a specimen. Finally, this insect is not bothered with bothersome caterpillar or chrysalid stages. Even the new-hatched phasmid is a perfect, diminutive twig.

In these few paragraphs I have tried merely to emphasize the exciting world which is hidden from us, in full daylight, by resemblance of light and shadow, colors and patterns, shapes and substance. It is sheer fun to find out the reason for resemblances and hideouts, whether because of the need of escape from watchful enemies or the lying in ambush for prey. We look at bark, flowers, seeds, grass, leaves, lichens, twigs, branches, stones, even bits of bird droppings, and a second glance may resolve them into hidden life. An irregular, splinter-topped dead stump may be a screech owl, a nubbin on a horizontal branch may be a camouflaged, lengthwise perching whippoorwill. The discovery and unraveling of these things are full of interest for us, but to the creatures themselves, they are matters of life and death. Enemies with a little better eyesight, living edible morsels with more watchful discernment, both might spell extinction, from starvation or from satisfying the hunger of another creature.

Get down on hands and knees, or lie prone or supine, and see what you will see.

CHAPTER 10

Too High To Be Seen

TO write honestly and with conviction anything about the migration of birds, one should oneself have migrated. Somehow or other we should dehumanize ourselves, feel the feel of feathers on our body and wind in our wings, and finally know what it is to leave abundance and safety and daylight and yield to a compelling instinct, age-old, seeming at the time quite devoid of reason and object.

We are concerned here only with the unseen in New York — the nocturnal aspects of bird migration. Most small birds migrate at night apparently with two outstanding advantages. The first is avoidance of attacks by hawks and other enemies, and second, the use of hours when feeding is impossible. Students of migration must blame these night activities for creating a mental hazard in themselves, of utter confusion. If all birds migrated in the daytime, migration might be explained, at least in part, as a matter of eyesight. Night voyaging upsets all such theories and we must admit we have no clear-cut explanation of how birds find their way through hour after hour, and night after night of darkness, and over hundreds and thousands of miles of land and sea.

In New York City there are three excellent methods of watching migration, and even if you do not know one bird from another, you cannot help being deeply interested by the instinct which carries these frail little beings up into dark, cold, naked space, perhaps a half mile above the planet.

Our first method is a daylight one and hence to be dismissed in a few words. It is the observation of the birds themselves, as at dawn they glide down from their lofty levels of flight, to trees and bushes on the ground. Here, in the hours of daylight, they must find time for sufficient restorative sleep and a frantic search for insects — to refuel their little stomachs for the energy needs of continued flight.

The second method is unique and requires only patience, a deck chair on a flat roof or lawn, a pair of binoculars and a full, or nearly full, moon. With the said moon at a reasonable elevation the procedure is simply to rest, relaxed, with eyes focused through the glasses on the bright satellite, and await what luck and chance offer.

Perhaps, already, faint chirps have hinted of passing migrants, and perhaps we have let our imagination play with the results of sudden daylight illumination. The heavens would be pitted and flecked with hundreds and thousands of flying birds. This we can never hope to enjoy, but the moon cuts a narrow swath of illumination through the sky. From two hundred and forty thousand miles away, down to our very retina, the darkness of night is penetrated by a tube of light, brilliant and transparent to our vision.

Your eyes may be focused on lunar deserts and craters, when a small black dot passes across the disk. Another follows and somehow your eyes become focused in midspace, and the third dot is recognized as a bird. Your neck will ache, your eyes tire, but your imagination and enthusiasm cannot flag. The very next speck may show a type of fluttering, or a looping dip which may identify the species or group. The birds in the moon will, forever afterwards, take precedence over the man in the moon.

The third method of watching migrants follows.

Many years ago (forty-nine to be exact, in 1904) I had a memorable experience watching birds on migration, high in the air, within the limits of Greater New York. In company with Madison Grant, Secretary of the Zoological Society, I obtained permission from the city authorities to spend a night in the top of the Statue of Liberty. This was about mid-May, a time when migration ought to be at its height. We caught the last boat to Bedloe's Island, and on its return trip it carried away the final sight-seer, reducing the population to the superintendent, his assistant, Mr. Grant and myself.

My first activity was rather comparable to mountain climbing. It was not the actual mounting of one hundred and sixty-eight steps from the base to the summit, but the difficulty of toting a blanket, lantern, food and binoculars up the narrow convolutions of the circular stairway. I finally had to make two trips, and unloaded in the crown of the noble goddess. As if I were planning an assault on Mount Everest, I made my base camp in the crown and my advance perch, or roost, in the torch.

In early evening, a downward look toward the water of the bay, three hundred feet below, showed the wakes of tugs and steamers, stretching out in long, well-defined lines, intersecting one another like the strands of a gigantic, waving cobweb. The day had been clear, but as the sun sank lower, clouds collected, and soon there began that most wonderful of earthly sights — an ever familiar, ever new sunset. The sun became obscured, but I knew when it sank below the hidden horizon by the sunset guns echoing from fort to fort.

Half an hour later the whole outlook had changed. After the beacon of the statue had been turned on, a feeling of complete isolation became very real, and the distant glimmering lights of the city made this sensation more intense. One felt suspended in mid-air with no apparent contact with sea or land.

I climbed the vertical ladder on to the narrow duckwalk around the torch itself and prepared to take a short nap before beginning my migration vigil. Hardly had I closed my eyes when a new characteristic of the copper giantess became apparent — she swayed. I was told this oscillation was through a twenty-four inch arc, back and forth, and that it had something to do with the safety stresses of the whole structure. As long as I remained conscious, the movement was soothing, somewhat like the swinging of a hammock. When sleep closed down, the mobility changed from oscillation to acceleration, and several times I awoke and sat up terrified, certain that the massive figure was hurtling to the ground. I have had a similar sensation three other times, in the midst of the sickening waves of a violent earthquake.

The night had suddenly turned cold, a breeze arose, and I changed my pallet to the wooden platform at the head of the stairway. With the rising wind the hollow statue came to life. During the day, with many people passing up and down, the echoes would be confused and not particularly noticeable. With the absence of humanity and the presence of a wind, the sounds become weird and awesome. I dropped a loose bolt which I had picked up, and the reverberations increased by echoes and distance, until from far down they sounded like thunder on distant mountains. The scratching of a pin was taken up and magnified until the screekings died out in uttermost coppery hollows. When I laughed and shouted aloud, there resulted a pandemonium of tortured devils yelling back at me. Long after all seemed quiet, a faint squeak, squeak, came softly to the ear, perhaps a mouse feeding on crumbs dropped by some sight-seer.

At eleven o'clock I mounted again to the torch. The wind had quieted down, but haze was drifting up the bay and down from the sky. Every few seconds the sound of bird voices came from overhead; the peet-sweet of a sandpiper, the croak of perhaps a green heron, the thin notes of warblers, and the more palpable chirps of sparrows. The haze changed to fog, and now, to the chorus of bird voices, there was added the occasional, distant, sonorous bass of a foghorn. Several times birds called from below my level, and then, without warning, something hurtled past my head, struck, and fell at my feet — a warm, palpitating but dying magnolia warbler.

The most surprising event of the entire night was a burst of song from two birds, heard a half hour apart. The first, I am certain, was a red-eyed vireo. Five of the brief, thrushlike phrases came to my ear. The first was dim in the distance, three others were hurried and close, one as the bird actually passed almost within sight. The fifth was half lost in a foghorn. The second song was the unmistakable four-syllabled utterance of a goldfinch. A single phrase came out of the fog, then the beginning of a second, apparently given as the bird passed, for the call rose into an indeterminate screech as it receded into the distance. I wondered at the emotion — a perfect example of displacement behavior — which prompted such an utterance under such inappropriate conditions.

As the fog increased and condensed in the warmth to almost rain, birds began to pass through the periphery of illumination, then to strike intermittently against railing and glass. I crouched low behind what protection I could find, to avoid being hit. One warbler flew against my coat and sank down panting. They came in waves, a few scattered birds, then a mob, swift and dense as a swarm of golden bees. All appeared bright and shining as they passed. Occasionally a dozen or more would seem to come in obliquely to the general line of flight, and at slower speed. In this case they would all keep on to the light, but put their feather brakes on in time, so that I would have five or six sparrows clinging to me at one time, unharmed, wings spread, heads back, panting.

For the period of a few hours I was permitted to share the feelings and activities of birds on migration, sensing altitude, isolation, darkness, wind, speed, and the awful confusion and dangers of light-in-fog.

At three o'clock in the morning the fog had lifted, and there was neither sight nor sound of the birds. They had flown down somewhere to a precarious landing in the thinning fog, or had reascended to migration levels. I climbed again into the torch and watched for the first hint of dawn and life. The first came almost imperceptibly as a pale line of gradually brightening light; the latter was startling. A herring gull, all gray and white, swung swiftly toward me from the direction of the sea, shrieked when it saw my muffled figure and passed up river. The gull presented a double surprise for at this time of year it must have been a maverick of sorts, and should have been with its fellows on some distant breeding grounds. Prosaic tugs appeared and smoke arose from a hundred chimneys: a new day had begun over New York City.

I descended and joined Mr. Grant. He had been with me for an hour of migration watching, but after that had chosen to finish the night in a guest room at the foot of the statue. Later on, we picked up two hundred and seventy-one dead birds on the ground around the base. We were told of one tragic night when more than fourteen hundred lost their lives. Thanks to the protests of bird lovers and especially half-dazzled pilots of passing vessels, the light of the statue was diminished and rendered indirect, so that, in more recent years, there have been very few avian casualties. A visit today to the great Statue of Liberty must be as memorable as ever, except that access to the torch is no longer open to the public.

In the intervening half century Miss Liberty has witnessed many radical changes within her field of view. Perhaps the most spectacular are the nonmigratory airplanes which roar past day and night, guided by compass, radio, radar and other direction-finding gadgets. Far overhead numberless birds are still passing, exactly as they have for thousands upon thousands of springs and autumns, guided by means which still are a mystery to us.

CHAPTER 11

Too Familiar To Be Seen

English Sparrow

The relation of the common English sparrow to mankind is an intricate business. From farther back than when man first learned to speak and to record, this bird has made its home throughout Europe and Siberia.

Carl Linnaeus in 1758 gave it a definite scientific name. About one hundred years later, living birds were imported into Brooklyn by the Honorable Nicholas Pike and other directors of the Brooklyn Institute, all of whom ought to have known better. Throughout the horse age sparrows were superabundant, but when the era of automobiles arrived, gasoline failed to replace the vitamins of half-digested oats. What an atomic age may do to *Passer domesticus* remains to be seen.

These birds come under our legend of "too familiar to be seen" for what is common, continual and monotonous in our environment, like the chirp of a cricket or a sparrow, soon ceases to affect our conscious senses. Yet this humble sparrow offers an epitome of the evolution of birds. The scales on its feet and legs are still unchanged from the covering of lizard ancestors, and the feathers themselves are only scales which have split up and frayed into soft plumes. The cock sparrow has a remarkable change of color. In winter his throat is a veiled grayish, but in spring the pale tips of the feathers become brittle and break off, revealing a solid expanse of contrasting black, beneath. This is really a change of pattern without actual alteration of pigment.

The courtship of the sparrow is a regrettably plebeian affair. The first phase is sheer exhibition of charm on the part of the male — strutting, fluttering, trailing of wings in an absurd jiggling dance. If results are not immediately forthcoming, or if rival males appear, the affair degenerates into a rough-and-tumble, catch-as-catch-can, with no holds barred. Carl Linnaeus, father of zoological nomenclature, expresses this in no uncertain terms, when he sums up the characteristics of *Fringilla domestica*, as *"Salacissimus qui vigesies saepe coit."*

When I was about fourteen years old I made a collection of bird nests, and had I only known it, I was on the brink of a very interesting ornithological discovery. I took the nest of an English sparrow from behind the blinds of my room, and find this note in my journal: "All of my other sparrow nests are open like a cup, except that of the house sparrow, which is like a ball with the entrance in one side. Why is this?"

Years and years after this momentous slip, a student of birds found the answer. He investigated the bones of the palate and other structures, and found that the English sparrow was not a sparrow, but a member of the family of weaverbirds of Africa, which build covered nests.

Red Jungle Fowl

Under modern urban conditions the normal habitat of the race of chickens in New York City is in the refrigerator or on the menu. But within our hundred-mile circle there are many chicken farms and abundant testimony that, to mankind, this is the most important bird in the world. Unlike some other domestic animals, the ancestry of the domestic fowl is well known. All kinds, breeds, sizes and colors of poultry have come to us through selective breeding of the red jungle fowl, *Gallus gallus*, of Asia.

This Unseen Ancestor, in appearance, calls to mind the breed of domestic fowl known as red game. In the wild bird, the colors in general of the head, neck and back are orange-red, with the tail and undersurface dark, glossed with green and purple. In its native Indian home each wild jungle fowl almost invariably mates and associates with from one to three hens. She hides her nest with great skill and deposits four to eight eggs. The wing muscles of the cock are strong and his flight can be as swift and direct as that of a pheasant. His weight varies from one and three quarters to two and a quarter pounds. His voice is a sharp, far-carrying, clear-cut double note, in striking contrast to the long-drawn-out, cock-a-doodle squawl of the barnyard bird.

Our degenerate chanticleer may weigh as much as thirteen pounds, it may be black, white, buff, brown, red or gray, and usually has a harem of twelve to twenty hens. Each of these has a potential capacity of more than two-hundred-fifty eggs in the course of a year. Courtship is a perfunctory affair, a little strutting, a brief dragging of a wing tip in the dust.

At the period of mating the wild bird encircles the hen with mincing, dainty steps, and all the wing and body plumage is flattened and sloped in the direction of his mate. Throughout the performance both birds never cease to send keen glances in every direction, on constant guard against dangers from jungle and from air.

At dawn the domestic bird still feels an itching of the wings, and claps his weak-muscled flight feathers together before crowing. After this he jumps or half flops down from his perch in the chicken coop. The wild bird glides smoothly down from his lofty bamboo perch, swiftly passing across the gorge to his feeding place. Then and then only will he utter his challenge.

Comparison is hardly fair between domestic and wild birds, the changes which have taken place in the generations have been of man's choosing; transforming a virile, alert, pheasantlike bird into an egg factory, an overdeveloped, flesh-laden parody of the original red jungle fowl.

Cockroach

The hot lush jungles which thrived in various parts of the world 250 millions of years ago, were composed of giant forebears of some of our lowliest plants. If we lie flat in a humid, Vermont woodland we will have an ant's-eye view of the scene and the Carboniferous flora will become more real to us. The ferns were then sixty feet high; instead of inchling horsetails, their heads waved stiffly in prehistoric breezes ninety feet above the ground. Our lowly, creeping club-mosses were then massive trees, one hundred feet high, with trunks five feet through. Through these weird forests there roamed no mammals or reptiles, no bird flew over them, because none had as yet been evolved to roam. Finally, the humid swamps deepened, the trees and other plants turned to peat and then to coal. Fossils of creatures, as well as leaves, were preserved, and gave us an idea of the animal life. Two facts stood out: cockroaches were abundant, and so close to those living today that it requires a trained orthopterist to distinguish them. So successful in the days of 250 million years back were these little beings, that no overt change has been required up to the last blattid to scuttle behind the kitchen sink. It is hard to tell whether this is to be considered as pre-eminent success or the epitome of *status quo*.

Before mankind came to offer havens of refuge, and repasts of delectable garbage, roaches were wood roaches, and today in the debris of tropical jungle floors they are often the most abundant insects.

What I have just written of the ability of continued existence almost unchanged throughout untold ages, brings to a focus a wider aspect of the subject. Perfection is a characteristic which is widely and indiscriminately applied in the present day. We read of perfect speeches, crimes, scores, and so we must admire the cockroach for a real perfection; that of adaptation to existence on this planet. There is no insect runner-up. *Cucaracha* in this respect is supreme.

We have already labored his existence in geologic time. There remain space, diversity, food, escape, habitat, eggs, parental care, precocity, and, in fact, many other divisions of a cockroach's life on the planet. Until the coming of man the various species were more or less isolated on their particular continents or islands, but with the arrival of man and ships, railroads and airplanes, the sky and the deep sea are the only out-of-bounds for this king of tourists.

Explorers have recorded the presence of roaches in the

K

skin robes of Eskimos (probably as transients from the explorer!). I have found them under a stone within reach of the salt spray from crashing breakers, and as high as I have been up in a tropic tree, I have seen them creeping happily about still higher.

At midnight, brown roaches come to our laboratory lights and yet in full sunlight more brightly colored forms fly through the jungle. Roaches are surprisingly few in numbers of species, apparently another adaptation — each species fitting its niche so well, or spreading this same niche to a world-wide extent. Thus there is no need for other than Smiths and Joneses in Blattville.

Roaches are essentially vegetarians, but this diet is of unlimited application. If they were scavengers only, we could put up with them better, but when, in one night, they completely eradicate the gilt titles on an entire row of entomological books, even the tolerance of a scientist is stretched to breaking point. A single application of ordinary varnish will foil their literary enthusiasm, whereas even 10 per cent DDT they seem, at times, to consider as a new vitamin of sorts.

To continue our list of perfection adaptations, the facility of escape must have played a large part in the continuity of roach existence. They are primarily thigmotactic — which is to say that they feel safer when in a narrow or flat confined space, so roach-sized that they can feel contact on as many sides as possible. In other words, a narrow crack is a roach's idea of a perfect refuge, if not, indeed, home. We know that the same individual roach may return, night after night, to the same crack, so the idea of a domicile may here have its inception.

In facility of reaching the said crack, a roach excels. So swift of foot is he that only an accomplished tap dancer could be certain of crushing him within the confines of a kitchen floor. In extremity he can almost emulate his cousin grasshopper in jumping ability, and as a last resort his wings come into play and carry him through the air, exactly as did the almost identical wings of his distant ancestors of the coal age. In a number of species the female is wingless, a physiological gesture, as if to show that a roach cannot lose even when handicapped.

The eggs are laid in cylindrical egg cases like little purses or beans, and the eggs are relatively few in number. This is another proof of the surviving ability of the roach, in this instance, the young, to take care of itself in spite of enemies. The female carries the case about for a few days, and this may be the dawn of maternal solicitude, rendering possible the selection of a safe place to deposit her packet. There is good need for this worry, for enemies are legion. There is a whole group of parasitic wasps which deposit their lethal ova nowhere but in the eggs of cockroaches.

A most vivid instance of the precocity of roach infants occurred on my laboratory table in British Guiana, when I recorded it more than thirty years ago. As I sat at the table something suddenly flew swiftly past my face and alighted clumsily among my vials and instruments. I saw it was a gigantic wood roach, all browns and grays, with marbled wings, strange as to pigments and to size, but with the unmistakable head and poise and personality of a New York Archy. The insect had flown through the rain and into the open window, but a second glance showed that it was in dire extremity, being in the grasp of a two-inch ctenoid spider. The eight long legs held firmly, but had not been able to prevent the roach from flying. At the moment of alighting the spider shifted his grip and secured the wings so that further escape was impossible. Both were desirable specimens and I instantly slipped a deep glass dish over them, and continued my microscope work.

Some time later I looked up and saw a strange sight. The spider still clung tenaciously to its victim, but the wood roach had her revenge. She was barely alive, yet within a few minutes she had changed from a strong, virile creature to an empty husk, seemingly dry and hollow, while over her and the spider, over glass and table-top scurried fifty exceedingly active little roachlets. They had burst from their mother or her egg case fully equipped and ready for life, leaving her a veritable husk, the ghost of a roach. Tiny, green, transparent, fleet, they raced back and forth over the spider. He grasped in vain at their diminutive forms, at the same time still clutching the dying, flavorless shred of a mother roach, holding fast as though he hoped that this unnatural miracle might reverse itself at any moment, and his victim again become fat and edible.

This adventure of the wood roach, this resolution of one into fifty, made wonderfully vivid the reproductive powers of tropical creatures. When in a moment of time, relatively speaking, a single insect can be resolved into half a hundred active, functioning duplicates of herself, the chance for survival of the more delicately adapted is faintly understandable. Here was spontaneous generation with a vengeance.

Once, in a Bornean jungle, I came across the branch-thatched couch of an orangutan. Almost fresh leaves showed it to have been built the night before. I climbed up to it and began to disentangle the components, to try to learn something of the architectural methods. As I pulled away a good-sized branch, three roaches scuttled out and off. It seems now, to me, that this was a fitting imaginary beginning to the infiltration of roaches into a first cave of some far-distant ancestors of ours, say a member of the Peking man clan, a half million years ago. And we wonder what was the reaction of our earliest grandparent. Did she ignore them, or, setting a habit of unnumbered generations to come, did she squash them? Or finally, do you suppose our distaff ancestor nibbled at them?

A psychological element enters into the scent of a roach, for, until we know the source, the odor of some species is not unpleasant. From Biblical times, and before, locusts and grasshoppers — close relatives of roaches — have played important parts on the menus of many nations.

But *cucarachas* seem to have been gastronomically immune.

Even in the matter of names, roaches are at semantic odds, at least in the matter of phonetics. The Latin name *Blatta* is unpleasant, invectivelike: "You Blattid, you!" But the Spanish sobriquet is pleasing, euphonious, and has even lent itself to a popular song, "La Cucaracha." It was left to an old friend of mine, Don Marquis, to make the cockroach a beloved character — Archy, the office cockroach, whose typewritten effusions were in lower case, because Archy could not manipulate the capital lever. One among many of his aphorisms was:

> i do not see why men
> should be so proud
> insects have the more
> ancient lineage
> according to the scientists
> insects were insects
> when man was only
> a burbling whatisit.

Fish to Frog

Almost all animals carry within their bodies traces of their ancestors. It has been stated that we ourselves possess as many as sixty of these ancestral evidences. The fold of skin in the inner corner of our eye is the remains of a third eyelid, dark glasses of sorts, which is present and useful in frogs and birds. The pineal in ourselves, is a concealed gland of uncertain function, whereas in some living lizards it is still a functional third eye. So much for the rags and tags of bar sinisters, half-forgotten traces of our former lives, handed on to us.

What is unimaginable would be a creature which hatched out before our eyes in the form of a lizard and grew up into a bird or a man. Equally marvelous would be the sight of a puppy developing into a whale. Such seeming absurdities take place only in geological time, throughout ages affording opportunities for extreme change, molding and adaptations to wholly new forms and spheres of life.

Yet within the confines of New York City one of the most common occurrences is as strange as the foregoing. Even in Central Park we may watch a fish change into a toad — which, from the point of view of modern-day evolution, of evolution while you wait, is sheer miracle.

Let us simulate evolution and start at the beginning. The ancient Phoenicians, Egyptians, Hindus, Japanese and Greeks all believed that the world was hatched from an egg. A similar development is at least true of every living thing upon the earth today; every plant springs from a seed, every animal from its egg. Still another sweeping, all-inclusive statement may be made — every seed or egg at first consists of but one cell, and by the division of this into many cells, the lichen, violet, tree, worm, crab, butterfly, fish, frog or other higher creature is formed. A little knowledge is good for any human being, whether it comes to him in watching the unfolding petals of an orchid, a caterpillar emerging from its egg, or a chick breaking through the shell.

Soon after toads and frogs have begun croaking and trilling, follow the sound to the nearest swamp or pond. Search among the dead leaves and sticks in shallow water until you find a string of long, black beads. Take home a jarful and put them in a saucer and make a day or a week memorable by watching them. The results will take your mind to pleasanter things than politics, crime and threats of war.

You will notice that the tiny spheres are not uniformly colored, but if the eggs have been recently laid the surface will be smooth and unmarked. Keep your eye on the little black and white ball of jelly, and before long, gradually, and yet with never a halt, a deep furrow makes its way across the surface, dividing the egg into equal halves. When it completely encircles the sphere you may know that you have seen one of the greatest wonders of the world. Before long, the unseen hand of life ploughs another furrow across the egg, and we now have four cells. These divide into eight, sixteen, and then on irregularly far beyond human powers of enumeration. Soon all the organs of a normal tadpole begin, develop and are ready for functioning when the polywogs or, literally, "wiggle heads" emerge.

A tadpole is not actually a fish, but many of its bodily

structures are fishlike, as is its method of swimming, hearing, breathing and the absence of limbs. All these combine to emphasize our simile of the evolution through the ages of primitive fishes into the higher land animals, up to and including ourselves. A tadpole becomes a toad in a matter of two months, but it is fair to compare this directly with the years it required to change a fish to a land animal. While this retaining of a fishlike ancestor as a larva facilitates the emergence into air, yet it tends to bind the adult to a humid zone. Hence, frogs and toads, when the time for breeding comes along, all return to the watery marshes or ponds of their ancestors.

The telescoped change is none the less wonderful for taking place in our present neighborhood and before our eyes. The tadpole has to get rid of its gills and develop lungs; it changes from a vegetable to an insect diet; its ear comes to the surface so it can hear the call of its mate in the air; the simple cartilaginous skeleton is altered to a bony one; the expanse of fin and tail must all be absorbed, and from new tissues, fingers and toes, arms and legs come into being, no trace of which existed in egg or newly hatched tadpole.

During the crisis of actual transformation the tadpole can neither eat nor drink nor hear, but must somehow keep alive during the shift in breathing and movement from water to air. If only a tadpole could possess self-consciousness, could say, "I am I," and later by some batrachian dictaphone or toad-script, could record his feelings and sensations as he metamorphosed, what an epic it would be! "Sixty Million Years in Sixty Days."

When the high-pitched trill, musical and long-continued, comes to our ears from the marsh, it should at least stir us with an emotion born of a little knowledge.

CHAPTER 12

Too Dark To Be Seen

IF we do not like the darkness of night we cannot blame it on the sun, for it is merely the absence of sunlight. On second thought, it is the earth itself which is at fault, for night is possible only because of the revolving of our old planet, turning one side after the other away from the sun for a number of hours. We think of night chiefly as an opportunity for sleep, and when it occurs to us, we give thanks that we live on a reasonable zone of earth, where the nights are not six months long.

Urban night life stresses theaters, the opera, night clubs, even baseball games, as well as burglars, astronomers and garbage collectors, to say nothing of the printing of the daily news almost before it has happened. As to our city fauna, pigeons, sparrows and dogs are diurnal, while cats still live in a pseudo jungle of their own, with fences instead of forest trees, and rubbish instead of underbrush.

For a long period of time eyes have played a conspicuous part in the evolution of life upon the earth, and we may well assume that daylight activities accompanied the development of primitive eyes. From time to time reversals took place. Various creatures found the darkness of night to be a welcome cloak of safety. Just as dolphins and whales have left solid earth and returned to the watery life of their far-distant forebears, so among all the squirrels of the world, flying squirrels alone sleep through the day and glide about in moonlight or in darkness.

There is a whole fauna adapted for life in darkness, and within our hundred mile circle around New York City, the night is filled with the activity of numbers of creatures. Some have made special niches for themselves, others seem to slip into the places vacated by beings of the day. For instance, in late afternoon, chimney swifts begin to disappear and are at once supplanted by the flickering of the first bats.

Speaking generally, creatures of the night depend less on the sense of sight than on hearing, smell and touch. On a night walk in the country near New York our ears may detect katydids and crickets, mosquitos, frogs and toads, owls, whippoorwills, night herons and the squeaks of bats and mice. In the tropics this list might be quadrupled, but it is a very respectable temperate suburban chorus.

Although, in the area we are considering, man and his works are dominant, yet no wild sound of the night has anything to do with his existence. In almost every case, the call of insect, amphibian, bird and mammal is intended solely for the ears of mate or family. The making of a sound implies the existence of an ear to hear, and the large ears of a field mouse are well fitted to receive the small squeak of another mouse. Male katydids vocalize by rubbing one wing against the other, and the receptive ear is located in the foreleg of the female. The song of the mosquito is, very reasonably, the hum of the wings of the female in flight. The vibrations of the hum are perfectly attuned to certain hairs on the antennae of the male, which are so oriented that they indicate not only the sound, but the direction as well, and so lead straight to the female mosquito.

Many frogs seem to depend less on individual, brief outbursts of sound, than on long-continued, massed orchestras. Their eyes are relatively enormous, able equally to detect a morsel of living food in motion, or an approaching mate. Onomatopoetic hoot and screech owls utter sounds which we describe as mournful, eerie or weird. To other owls they must be adequate and satisfactory. To small birds and rodents the same sounds carry implications of terror and death. The whippoorwill is cricketlike in its vocal brevity of phrase and its insistency.

The diurnal vertical slit in the irises of such animals as some frogs and in cats is of the nature of a dark glass, an excellent adaptation to reduce the glare of daylight. This permits the better functioning of the oversensitive, fully open eye, making use of every ray of the dimmest nocturnal illumination. Owls and whippoorwills, curiously enough, although essentially birds of the night, have kept the rounded pupil of daylight livers, and are compelled to close their lids to slits to diminish daylight glare.

To the fact that none of the nightly sounds are intended for our ears, must be added that our hearing is too limited and imperfect to record many of these calls. Now and then we hear the high, shrill squeak of a passing bat, or a succession of them when a cluster of these creatures is disturbed, hanging from the roof of their favorite cave or eave. The reason why a bat never collides or bumps against an obstacle is because of its perfect sonar apparatus. The audible squeak ends when the (to us) inaudible sound waves begin; these, rebounding from the nearest obstacle, are re-echoed to the great ears, as a warning. The obstruction may be a brick wall, a dangling thread or a flying moth — the warning comes in time to dodge, or to seize and devour. How any one individual out of a flock of sonaring bats can distinguish its own particular echo, and act on it, is still a mystery.

Many creatures doubtless find the darkness a haven of safety from enemies, but some of these pursuing enemies, like shrews and owls, have followed their victims into the night, to seek them out and attack from the ground, or, in the latter case, to launch their assaults from mid-air.

In the matter of nocturnal scents and odors, our corresponding human sense organs are so faulty that they are of little help in satisfying our curiosity. An interesting experiment is to place a beetle, a moth, a bug, an ant and a grasshopper, each in a separate, corked vial, and after a few minutes, to open and sniff. Although bound on the wheel of our sensory handicap, we will be surprised into unexpected exclamations — pleased, disgusted, pained or just negative. One vial may pour forth attar of roses, the second an odor of carrion, another as sharp as ammonia, still another with no detectable scent. Each, to the right organism, must have borne a message, perhaps vital, alluring, an olfactory chit of life or death. Only the continued exhalation of the essences in a confined space renders them apparent to our nostrils.

Many moths excell in their amazing detection of attenuated odors. This ability seems to lie in antennal hairs, and may lead the owner over hill and dale, a mile or more upwind, to a caged female.

The opossum is common about New York but is an anomaly. It is nocturnal, and, as I have said before, it possesses an extremely unpleasant odor, it is widely hunted and is excellent as food, it is the dominant victim of passing automobiles, and whenever encountered, its usual reaction is only to "play possum," to simulate death. Yet it seems to thrive more than most wild creatures hemmed about by humans.

The nocturnal skunk bases its immunity on notoriety, for its battery of high-explosive scent would soon be exhausted, were it not that most of the creatures it encounters (including humans) recognize its latent powers of defense. It is the mammalian epitome of a living atomic bomb.

Touch is one of the dominant senses of the night, but, unlike hearing and smelling, it requires actual contact. With a flashlight, a close watch on the leaves and bark of the countryside will reveal the tap-tapping sources of nocturnal insects and other organisms, feeling out a way of life leading to food or mate or death.

Moles make their own perpetual night, living alone in their endless tunnels, only rarely breaking through the crust to seek a mate. Again the little animal sinks from sight, to bring forth as few as two infant moles, a significant number when compared with the innumerable offspring of field mice.

The ultimate, perfect adaptation to darkness, to active life at night, is the illumination of the firefly. This is no creeping odor or evanescent, radiating sound, but a direct attack on the darkness, the manufacture and flaunting of a little day — each gleam a diminutive sun whose rays momentarily defeat the gloom.

There are four or five species of firefly beetles which live within our New York circle. As a rule the females do not use their wings and some are totally wingless. Their part is to climb as high as possible to the tip of a grass blade and hang out their living lantern. It is a steady beacon to attract anything but a "blind date." Instinct has developed a specific, make-and-break Morse code, an individual rhythm, recognizable only by the appropriate male. His flashing, as he flies here and there, stimulates her to increase her response. One advantage of this interrupted flashing is that any long-continued glow would be as likely to attract enemies as mates.

This wonderful heliographic method of assuring the continuation of the race has occasional tragic aspects. One of our New York firefly female exhibits considerable variety in her flashes. Like the notes of the brain-fever bird of India the exact number of gleams is uncertain. Now and then she unwittingly gives forth the private signal code of another species, which is soon responded to by a passing male. The error is instantly recognized by the female, who, instead of intimating "Sorry, wrong number," seizes and devours the unfortunate, unrelated male, victim of her own erroneous flashing.

Most females have a "go signal" of greenish-blue, but here again the matter may be more complex than it appears, for some males are more sensitive to red, so perhaps fireflies are color blind and it is the intensity, rather than the color, which attracts them.

Years ago I wrote about the flashing in unison of fireflies, especially those in the Far East — the most striking

L

and mysterious of their activities. I even coined a new word, that the trees were candelabraed with fireflies. Hundreds of these insects fly at evening to a certain kind of tree, a definite individual tree, cover its limbs and twigs and then flash and dim, flash and dim, in perfect rhythm. No female is in sight, so the performance has nothing to do with courtship. It may continue for weeks or months, a regimented display interrupted only by the full moon.

The most brilliant light of a firefly may equal one fiftieth candle power, or corresponding to the illumination reaching us from the first magnitude star Canopus. Man has never been able to imitate or even approximate the glow of the firefly, for it is practically light without heat.

I have intentionally treated this chapter, "Too Dark To Be Seen," in a sporadic, factual way to emphasize the discontinuous, fact by fact manner of any study of life-in-darkness. When once we leave the revealing light of day we are in a class with the blindmen and the elephant. Yet its importance is manifest when we remember that half of the entire life of every creature is spent in the mystery of night.

CHAPTER 13

Too Deep To Be Seen

THE best-known Hudson Terminal is a tunnel in lower New York built a few decades ago. The original Hudson Terminal is a canyon, one hundred miles southeast of New York City, lying one mile below the surface, and excavated sometime around a million years ago. This canyon is a crack in the doorstep of the city, and lies on the continental shelf, bordering the Atlantic coast, and extending far out beyond Sandy Hook.

The exact method of formation of this mighty Hudson River Gorge is still uncertain, but we know that the area which lies deep beneath the turbulent waters was once part of a great river system that drained not only the Hudson Valley, but the valleys of the Great Lakes, and the present Connecticut, Housatonic, Passaic and Hackensack rivers.

When our own Hudson was in its glory the great glaciers of the ice age had not yet filled its bed with boulders and gravel as it is today. In that past time the Palisades rose four times as high above the water as they do today. The river flowed seaward 45 miles beyond the present coastline, then dropped first over an 1800 foot waterfall, then three others, until the canyon lost itself in the level bed of the uttermost depths.

A matter of about twenty thousand years ago we might have walked far out, along the river of the gorge, for the last advancing glacier had locked up so much water in its icy embrace that the level of the entire ocean was lowered several hundred feet. Thus, because of the erosion of past ages, the creatures living at a mile depth are today brought within the limits of our New York circle.

A few years ago I made a small expedition to investigate these primitive New Yorkers, and we must not forget, as I have said before, that far, far back in the dim mists of early evolution, we and they were one — so we may think of them as ancestral neighbors.

At present, visitors are taken daily on a sight-seeing yacht which steams around Manhattan Island and shows the city from a new point of view. The time will come when tourists, as well as native New Yorkers, will be able to board a ship, head seaward to the hundred-mile line, and in the course of a few hours watch "monsters of the deep" brought to the surface before their eyes, fresh from the black, icy depths. Meanwhile, a brief account of my own expedition will anticipate and envisage such a tour.

Late on a July evening, on the seagoing tug *Wheeler*, we backed slowly out from a Brooklyn slip. Our first attempts at sleep were interrupted by a magnificent, unseasonable display of northern lights — flashes and ribbons and radiating spokes of yellow and rose and green. At eight o'clock the following morning the little tug was rolling gently on the threshold of New York's abyssal world, something more than one hundred miles out at sea, with the ultramarine of open ocean stretching all around to the rim of the world. The only life on the planet seemed to be our tugful of selves and a quartet of Mother Cary's Chickens.

The small *Arcturus* winch was uncovered, given a breath of steam, and the wire began to uncoil. To it a series of great silken nets was attached, and they went billowing back in the wake of the tug, settling slowly out of sight. A mile and a half of wire was run out and for several hours we crawled along at a speed of barely two knots. I put my hand on the taut, vibrating spider web of steel, my eye followed it down into invisibility into the liquid blue, and the underworld of the deep sea became very real. I have walked in comfort, in a metal helmet, ten fathoms deep; once I exceeded a half mile straight down in the Bathysphere, but in general, the North Pole is far more accessible than where the nets were being drawn. At the surface of the water, temperature is 68 degrees; five hundred fathoms down it is 40 degrees, and at the bottom of the Hudson Gorge the thermometer would read 31 degrees. In this unbelievable world, not only does bitter cold prevail, but complete and eternal darkness, and the pressure, at a mile depth, of a ton to each square inch.

Finally I waved my hand, the bell in the engine room clanged, the idling propeller rested and the sturdy bulk of the tug began to roll, swinging to the wind. Slowly the wire reeled in, and after a long time the great nets, at their apex, came dripping and cold to the surface and were drawn on board. Our final count showed fifty-five species of deep-sea fish, of which five were new to science.

Into big jars and aquariums were poured the pink treasure, glittering and gleaming, trembling with strange vitality, every spoonful a cosmos of hundreds of living creatures. There loomed through the translucent mass a long black and bronze eel, or, as it finally proved, a nine-inch scimitar-fanged sea dragon. I picked it up and at the first touch felt almost pain from the bitter cold. In the heat of a still July day, my hands became numb as I dipped them into the glistening gelatin, and the strange character of this deep world began to shape itself in my mind.

As I picked up the dragonfish, the mouth opened unbelievably wide, as wide as would be the gape of a saber-toothed tiger, and the long needle-sharp fangs came together with a snap. I had wondered how the teeth could be managed, and I now saw that the two longest went straight through concealed grooves in the head and appeared above the skin near the eyes. A long tentacle thread from the dorsal fin drooped forward in advance of the head. Later by accident the fish bit upon my fingers, but so weak had exposure to these surface pressures rendered the creature, that the tips of the needle fangs did not even pierce my skin.

Several large shrimps caught my eye, for they were of the most intense flaming scarlet. I put one into a small glass, ran down to a dark cabin, shut the door and watched magic. Little by little, from out of several pores there flowed a fluid within fluid — a foggy mist sifting and billowing through the water, a mist which suddenly took fire and in the darkness I saw I was holding a glowing glass — the water alight with soft radiance. As a squid escapes through his own sepia smoke screen, so this deep-sea shrimp was covering his being with a dazzling cloud of fire. A second realization came to me — the utter darkness along the path of the net. Sixty feet below the surface I have watched fish swim in what seemed tropical moonlight. Even at this slight depth the red end of the spectrum goes first. So at his infinitely greater depth, the scarlet shrimp would be black as night, or his surroundings, there being no reflected red rays. Until I brought him to the surface he was not and had *never* been red.

We think of the darkness and we see the great fangs and we see a relation between the two. Plants cannot grow without sunlight, so, far beneath the surface, every creature is carnivorous. We know that some are cannibals, and others have a stomach so elastic that they can swallow a fish several times their own length.

If absolute and perpetual midnight should suddenly envelop our city, only those of us could survive who had access to adequate illumination, or who by blind skill could manage to avoid danger and find food. As we study our deep-sea creatures we learn that the same thing holds good in the gorge of the Hudson. Many of the fishes, shrimps and squids are covered with powerful searchlights, or dotted with lesser beacons, and their eyes are large and far-seeing. In other creatures we find long feelers reaching out in all directions and associated with blind or nearly blind eyes. As a blind man hangs a lettered sign about his neck — a sign he himself can never read — and sits patiently waiting for it to attract pennies, so occasionally we find a blind fish with the sockets of its eyes turned into glowing headlights. We can explain this only as a lure to draw small victims close enough for some other sense to detect them.

In every net there are many unsolved problems. A tiny white thread of a fish, which we scoop into a glass of sea water, has perfectly good eyes far out on the ends of slender stalks, each half as long as the body. The life history of these stalk-eyed dragonfish would be considered sheer fantasy were it not scientifically factual. If the fish were shaped like a human being the length of the stalks would locate the eyes on the tips of the fingers, most efficient for watching a passing parade, but of no use to the fish that we know of. These are very young, but as the fish grows older the eye-stalks begin to shorten and draw the eye nearer the head. The cartilage skeleton is absorbed, the nerve crumples and twists and finally, is actually crowded down into vacant eye sockets, ready for it. The eye follows, is drawn close, and takes root.

From now on the eyes of the stalk-eyed dragonfish are just where we find them in all normal fish. Another phase of the strange life begins. The sexes commence to diverge, the female increasing rapidly in size, until she measures almost a foot in length, turning black, developing a row of shining portholes along her sides, and a large brilliant beacon near the tail, all luminous pink. She also grows an elaborate, leaflike, chin barbel and a terrifying set of fangs.

The male remains dwarfed, two inches over-all, and is almost transparent. His mouth is toothless and he can neither ingest nor digest food. A great light appears on each side of his head with an efficient reflector and he barges slowly along through life, hoping against hope that a mate will find him before he dies of starvation. That all this is a very real handicap is shown by there being many more males than females. What a life! Shining forth his twin lamps, he watches always for the thousand and one chance that a form, approaching through the utter darkness, is not an implacable enemy but one of his own kind.

In spite of all these obstacles the species seems to prosper. They have been found in almost every sea, and in two seasons of deep-sea trawling in Bermuda we took more than a hundred, most of them a full mile down. Off New York, on the present trip, two stalk-eyed dragonfish found their way into the nets.

In the depths of the sea hundreds of little fish are swimming, all exactly alike, less than two inches long, tail fins wagging furiously, eyes striving to glimpse some friendly spark of light in all the eternal darkness. Their nostrils are very large, ready to detect the faintest hint of an odor. The jaws are produced into a sort of snout like a pair of pincers, each armed with a cluster of toothlike spines. In addition to complete external identity, every one is a male. In the Hudson Gorge, in one of the deepest nets, we found two of these dwarf males. So we can recount their known story as concerning our abyssal New York neighbors.

Thousands upon thousands of these small fish hatch, pursue their frantic search and perish. Or, through sight of a flaming globe, or the diffusion of a subtle odor, one, more fortunate, detects and approaches a great .creature one hundred times as large as itself — an unlovely, awkward, black fish, flaunting a yellow lantern on a long tentacle. Her eyes are minute, almost useless, and every inch of skin is covered with large, ivory-hard, sharp spines. Even among the dragons and gargoyles of deep-sea fishes, this abyssal fishing frog must be accounted ugly.

With a single gulp she could swallow a dozen of the little black fish if they clustered around her beacon. But for the one following close upon her scent the shining globe has no attraction. Like an iron filing drawn to a magnet, he rushes headlong upon her. He may strike upon her sides or back or even on her head. Wherever it may be, he seizes hold with his clusters of bristles, finding a tiny area of soft skin somewhere among the spines. Holding fast — like a burr to wool — he begins to gnaw with his teeth until he exposes a bit of raw flesh. In some manner, as yet unknown, the capillaries of the giant fish merge with those in his mouth, and a perfect union is formed of flesh and blood. Such is the marriage of the little bristle-snouted male with this huge, black, female lantern bearer.

Marvels only begin at this moment, for after the fusion is complete there sets in an appalling degeneration in the body of the small parasite. He loses eyes, nostrils, brain, bones, stomach. He is nourished by the life-giving blood of his strange mate; he is carried wherever she wishes to go; he is protected from harm by his smallness and his flabbiness, half-hidden among the horny, mountainous spines of his consort's skin. His only remaining destiny is to fertilize the eggs which in course of time stream out into the water. After this he may perish, or else, preserving whatever individuality is left, he may exist until his hostess succumbs, when, automatically, death comes to him.

Another fish is round and of glowing silver, and has all its batteries of green and violet lights directed downward, while its eyes forever stare immovably upward. A fourth fish has series of great curved teeth along the jaws, but outside, at various angles on the skin, where they seem utterly useless.

Now and then we see something which needs no explanation, but demands only appreciation and wonder; a curious, pale violet, humpbacked shrimp with a brood of tiny humpbacked offspring. All are gathered on the inside of a transparent, fluted barrel which the mother has taken from its original owner, and, like a more unselfish Diogenes, used it for a nursery. With her swimmerets she is able to kick her house along so that a stream of water and food pours through. Though hosts of hungry dragons may nose about the sides, yet the shrimp and her brood are safe. The courtships and battles, the comedies and tragedies of family life in this underworld seem to our over-imaginative minds to be tales of ingenuity, horror and devotion.

With all this strangeness there is also beauty. In and out through the mass of life swim active opals — gleaming and scintillating as they twist and turn — tiny, oval, living tissues of flame and ash, which glow as brightly after death, for their colors are due not to pigment but, like a hummingbird's throat, to a myriad prisms.

With our present meager facilities we can best revive the glories of the sea depths by taking the newly caught beings into a darkened room, and watch the shift and play of colored lights, the lines upon lines of glowing portholes, each beacon as complex as an eye, with lens and reflector; other lights arranged in certain patterns along the sides are for recognition by members of the same school, and finally, we watch the penetrating flashes which, as they are different in the two sexes, may be of use in finding and securing a mate.

With body cramped from a day of long and intensive inactivity, I am roused by a steady throbbing, and look up to see that the tug is heading homewards. Far off on the horizon is a tiny black smudge in the sky, and I realize that there is another world than this of the ocean deeps — that on the great liner on the horizon people are playing bridge, gossiping, looking at the water with unseeing eyes, while in the dimming light of day the sea dragons beneath their keel are swimming along on their tigerish quests in this Unseen World.

Conclusion

WE are now in the fourth interglacial period of warmth, and it seems absolutely certain that in the course of the usual thousands of years to come, the fifth glacier will begin its swing southward.

I remember, when a child in the year 1888, being drawn upon the top of the snow on a sled over the tips of the city's street lamps, and wondering if I should ever again see the streets or the ground. Sometimes at night when I look out upon a world of swirling snowflakes and listen to the howl of the bitter winter gale, it seems as if Labrador had already liberated glacier number five.

If we keep to the cosmic schedule, the inception and development of our present city occupy only a fleeting second of geological time, conservatively one forty millionth. What of the future? As I write, let us suppose hundreds of thousands of years have already passed. It is in the dim, distant future, and my faltering human mind can be certain of only one ultimate happening.

Let us visualize it. I came to the zoo a few weeks ago in a driving snowstorm. The Rocking Stone was capped with white, and, all around, the ground was a foot deep in millions of snow crystals. My imagination can conceive the next day and the next and the next as of continued storm; frantic messages come from Canada of a slow-moving continent of ice, coming nearer and nearer, of never-ending snow. From along all ocean shores come reports of the slow sinking of the sea itself, leaving the beaches bare and frozen.

All animals and human beings flee southward or perish. No man-made explosives or heating plants can do anything to stop the cataclysm for a moment. Soon come the last living creatures, polar bears whimpering with fear, snowy owls, musk oxen searching for a final bit of moss, walruses swimming down the coast. At last the enormous pale green ice front of cliff, a half or a full mile in height, crunches and grinds its way to the zoo, just as it has done twice before. The houses, everything, crumble like clusters of twigs and pebbles. Last of all, if there could be any human eye to see, the age-old Rocking Stone itself is stirred, pushed from its bed, and like a great snowball rolls slowly southward in the forefront of the glacier.

Another ice age is on its way!